1001 WINNING
CHESS SACRIFICES
AND COMBINATIONS

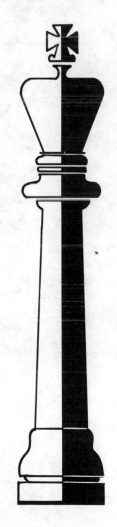

ABOUT THE AUTHOR

Howard Simon

FRED REINFELD is a native New Yorker. It was in the city schools and at City College that he began his chess-playing. While still in his teens he became Intercollegiate Champion, and was victorious in the New York State, Manhattan Club and Marshall Club Championship matches, beating such worthy opponents as Sammy Reshevsky, Reuben Fine, Arnold Denker and Al Horowitz.

Mr. Reinfeld has been one of the editors of "Chess Review" since its start in 1933. He is a prolific writer, with more than 50 chess books to his credit. On the staff of New York University, he teaches chess to hundreds of students yearly.

1001 WINNING CHESS SACRIFICES AND COMBINATIONS

by

FRED REINFELD

Published by
Melvin Powers
WILSHIRE BOOK COMPANY
12015 Sherman Road
No. Hollywood, California 91605
Telephone: (213) 875-1711 / 983-1105

OTHER BOOKS BY FRED REINFELD

EIGHTH BOOK OF CHESS: How to Play the Queen Pawn Openings

SEVENTH BOOK OF CHESS: How to Play the King Pawn Openings

SIXTH BOOK OF CHESS: How to Fight Back

FIFTH BOOK OF CHESS: How to Win When You're Ahead

FOURTH BOOK OF CHESS: How to Play the Black Pieces

THIRD BOOK OF CHESS: How to Play the White Pieces

SECOND BOOK OF CHESS: The Nine Bad Moves (and How to Avoid Them)

FIRST BOOK OF CHESS (with I. A. Horowitz, co-author)

CATALOGUE OF THE WORLD'S MOST POPULAR COINS

TREASURY OF THE WORLD'S COINS

COIN COLLECTORS' HANDBOOK

CASH FOR YOUR COINS

COINOMETRY: An Instructive Historical Introduction to Coins and Currency for the Young Collector (with Robert V. Masters, co-author)

COMPLETE BOOK OF CHESS OPENINGS

1001 WAYS TO CHECKMATE

URANIUM AND OTHER MIRACLE METALS

TREASURES OF THE EARTH

Third Printing

Copyright, 1955
by Sterling Publishing Co., Inc.

Manufactured in the United States of America

Library of Congress Card No. 55-7430

Printed by
HAL LEIGHTON PRINTING COMPANY
P.O. Box 3952
North Hollywood, California 91605
Telephone: (213) 983-1105

ISBN 0-87980-111-5

Table of Contents

CHESS NOTATION

As indicated in the following diagram, all the squares on the chessboard are *numbered* from both sides of the board; White's KR1, for example, is Black's KR8. Each square is also *named* for the piece occupying the file. Below the diagram is a list of the chief abbreviations used in chess notation.

BLACK

QR8	QN8	QB8	Q8	K8	KB8	KN8	KR8
QR7	QN7	QB7	Q7	K7	KB7	KN7	KR7
QR6	QN6	QB6	Q6	K6	KB6	KN6	KR6
QR5	QN5	QB5	Q5	K5	KB5	KN5	KR5
QR4	QN4	QB4	Q4	K4	KB4	KN4	KR4
QR3	QN3	QB3	Q3	K3	KB3	KN3	KR3
QR2	QN2	QB2	Q2	K2	KB2	KN2	KR2
QR1	QN1	QB1	Q1	K1	KB1	KN1	KR1

WHITE

King — K	check — ch
Queen — Q	discovered check — dis ch
Rook — R	double check — dbl ch
Bishop — B	en passant — e.p.
Knight — N	good move — !
Pawn — P	very good move — ! !
captures — x	outstanding move — ! ! !
to — —	bad move — ?

Sacrifices and Combinations

The man who wrote, "Tactics is 99 per cent of chess," might well have added—"and 99 per cent of the fun, too!" Brilliant sacrifices and combinations, either calculated in advance or played on the spur of the moment, give us thrills that cannot be equaled by any other aspect of the game. And, by a very fortunate coincidence, these brilliant strokes are just what we need in order to become first-rate players.

But then comes the practical question: How do we learn to become brilliant players? (Or is this a knack that one has to be born with?) The answer is reassuring: *Every chessplayer, no matter what his degree of skill may be, can learn how to play brilliant chess.*

The first step toward mastery is to become familiar with the different types of tactical motifs. The second step is to study a great many examples of these tactical themes. So, the object of this book is to add to your knowledge, to make you a strong chessplayer, and (last but not least) to delight you with some of the most beautiful moves ever played on the chessboard.

1. Pinning

The pin is by far the most frequently used tactical theme. It may be defined as *an attack on a piece which screens a second piece from attack*. The unit attacked in this way is said to be pinned. If attacked with enough force and ingenuity, it can often be won or completely disabled. Some examples:

In Diagram 2 Black's Knight is subject to an "absolute" pin. (This is the term we use when the King is the screened piece.) Worse yet, the Knight is pinned in two ways, by the White Queen and Bishop. And still worse, the Knight is not protected by a Pawn, which is the best—and cheapest—defense for a pinned piece. All these weaknesses combine to make possible White's brilliant demolition of Black's position.

In Diagram 5 we see again the fatal effect of an "absolute" pin. Once we're familiar with the pinning motif, we become used to the idea of *creating* pins—as for example in Diagram 16, where White first sacrifices in order to win Black's Queen by means of a pin.

Sometimes a pin defeats an already existing pin. Diagram 11 is a thrilling example of this.

A frequent use of the pin is to "pile up" on the pinned piece with an effective Pawn advance, as in Diagram 17. The piling-up may also be performed by pieces—sometimes with startling effect, as in Diagram 1.

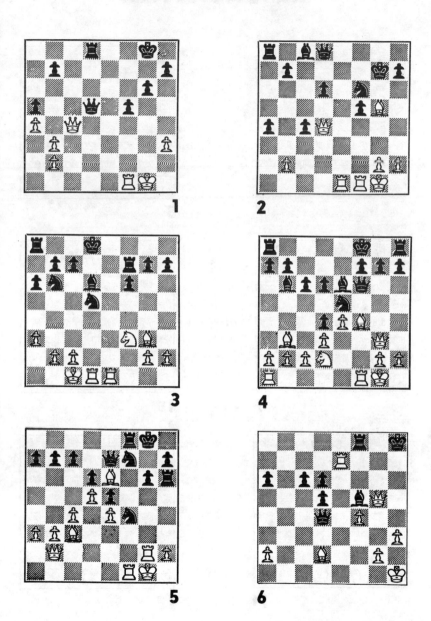

7

8

9

10

11

12

14 · PINNING ·

13

14

15

16

17

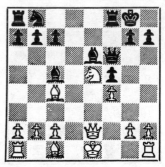

18

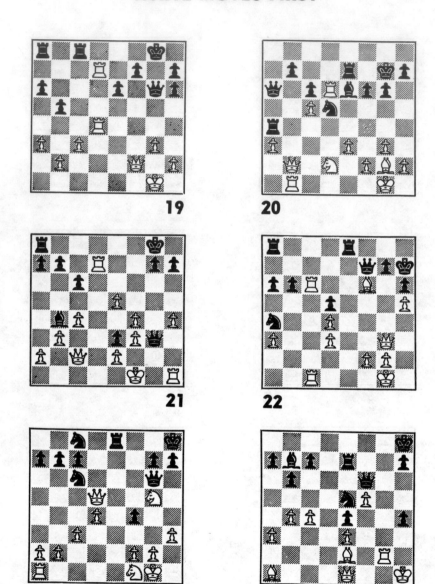

19

20

21

22

23

24

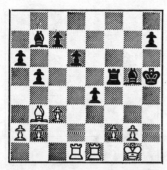

25

26

27

28

29

30

WHITE MOVES FIRST

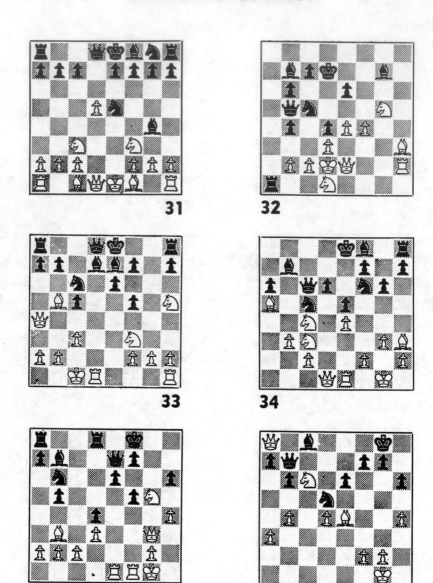

31

32

33

34

35

36

WHITE MOVES FIRST

37

38

39

40

41

42

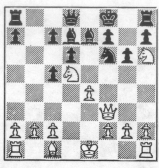

43

44

45

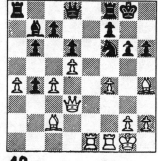

46

47

48

20 · PINNING ·

49

50

51

52

53

54

WHITE MOVES FIRST

55

56

57

58

59

60

22 · PINNING ·

61

62

63

64

65

66

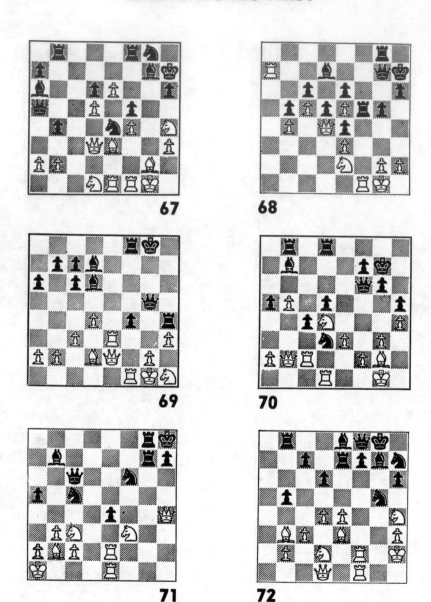

67

68

69

70

71

72

BLACK MOVES FIRST

73

74

75

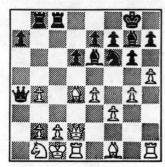

76

77

78

BLACK MOVES FIRST

79

80

81

82

83

84

26 · PINNING ·

BLACK MOVES FIRST

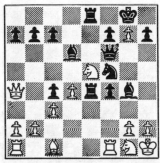

85

86

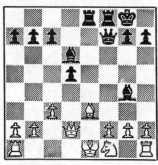

87

88

89

90

91

92

93

94

95

96

28 · PINNING ·

BLACK MOVES FIRST

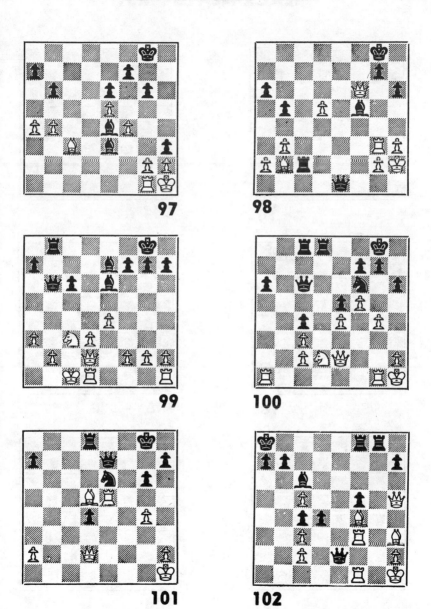

97

98

99

100

101

102

103

104

105

106

107

108

2. Knight Forks

The Knight fork is the most popular tactical theme aside from the pin. Actually, the Knight fork is a special case of the double attack—*an attack on two units by a single unit.* But the Knight fork is particularly effective, and particularly dreaded, especially by inexperienced players.

Sometimes the Knight fork appears in a fairly simple setting, as in Diagram 112, where it is merely necessary to give a Knight check as a preliminary to the winning fork.

In some cases a more or less subtle preliminary is needed to set the stage for the fork. Diagram 117 is a good example; Diagram 118 shows the same principle, but in a more elaborate form.

A Knight fork is often deadly in combination with a pin —as in Diagram 126.

Generally speaking, the most effective Knight forks are checks. Diagram 131 is a fine example: White attacks King and Queen; the King must move; the Queen is lost.

Finally, a Knight fork may often come at the very end of a combination, with an effect which is all the more powerful. See the sequence in Diagram 138, where White's weird-looking preliminary moves take on portentous meaning with the concluding Knight fork.

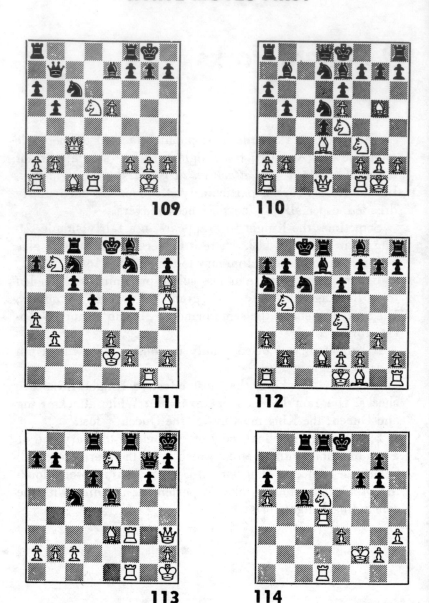

109 **110**

111 **112**

113 **114**

32 · KNIGHT FORKS ·

115

116

117

118

119

120

121

122

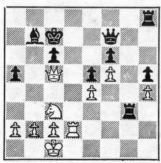

123

124

125

126

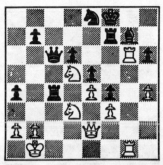

127

128

129

130

131

132

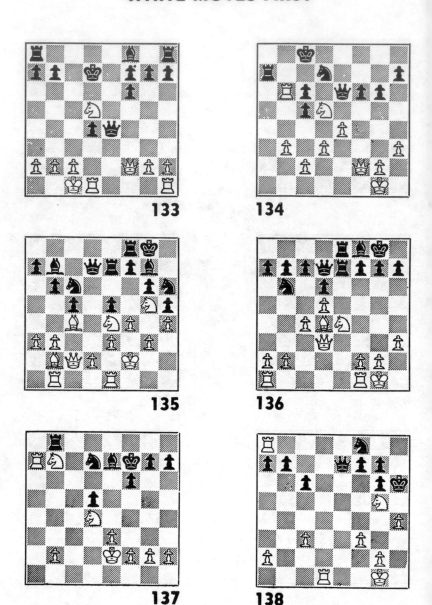

133

134

135

136

137

138

36 · KNIGHT FORKS ·

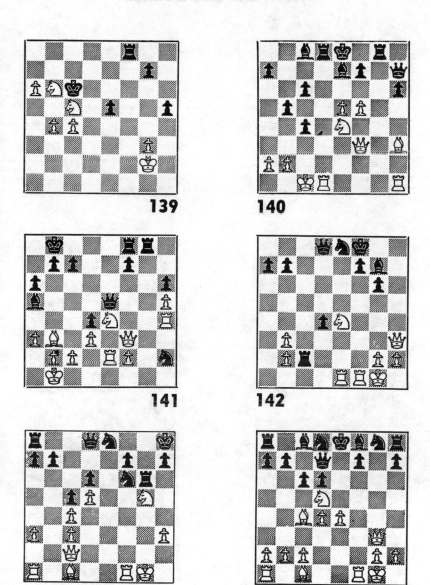

139   140

141   142

143   144

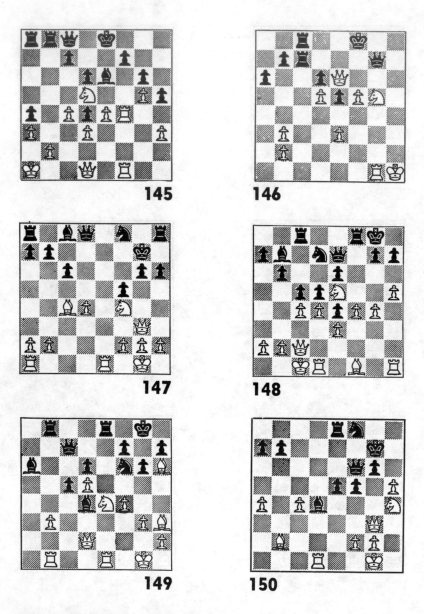

145

146

147

148

149

150

BLACK MOVES FIRST

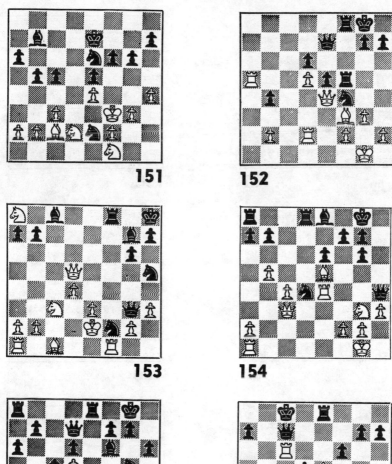

151

152

153

154

155

156

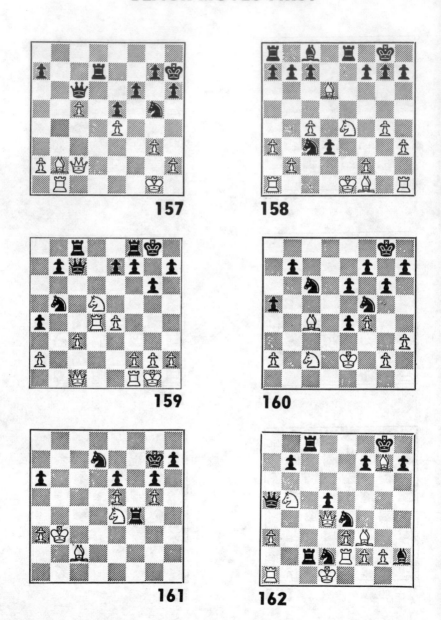

157

158

159

160

161

162

BLACK MOVES FIRST

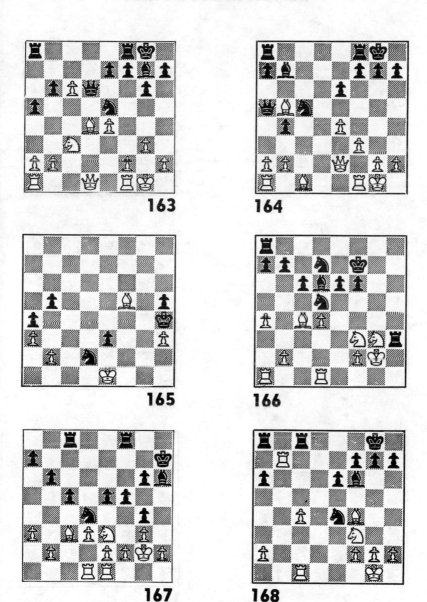

163

164

165

166

167

168

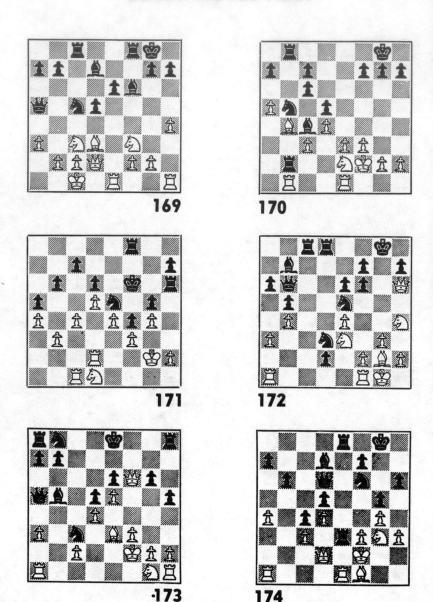

169

170

171

172

·173

174

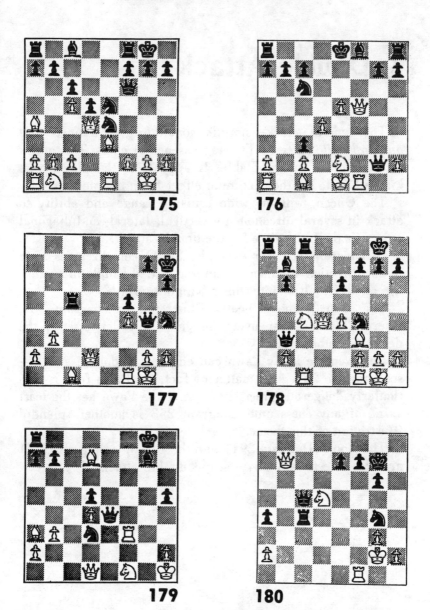

175

176

177

178

179

180

3. Double Attack

This type of attack—*simultaneous attack by a single unit on two hostile units*—is the very essence of chess. This attack is economical and profitable. It appeals to the player who knows how to get the maximum effect from his pieces.

The Queen, with its wide cruising range and ability to attack in several directions by vertical, lateral, and diagonal moves, is the ideal piece for the double attack.

In Diagram 181, for example, the Queen threatens mate in one direction and menaces an unguarded Knight in another direction. Result: White wins a Knight by force.

The same theme is neatly illustrated in Diagram 187, where White first maneuvers the Queen in order to set up the decisive double attack.

But even the lowly Pawn can engineer a double attack— see Diagram 225. As a matter of fact, the Pawn fork is particularly dangerous precisely *because* the Pawn has the least value of any chess unit. Diagram 253 is another splendid illustration of this theme.

The Rook (Diagram 291) and the Bishop (Diagram 277) are also effective in carrying out double attacks.

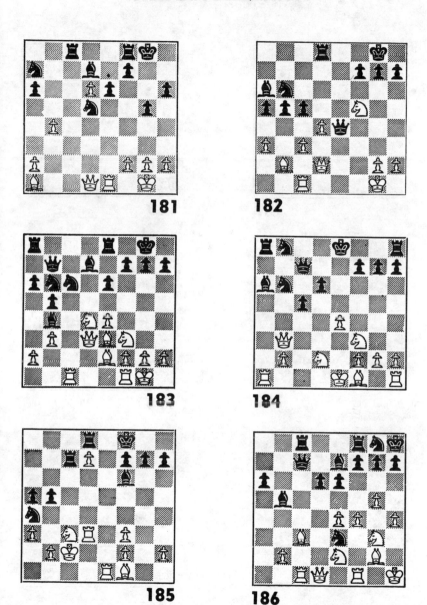

181

182

183

184

185

186

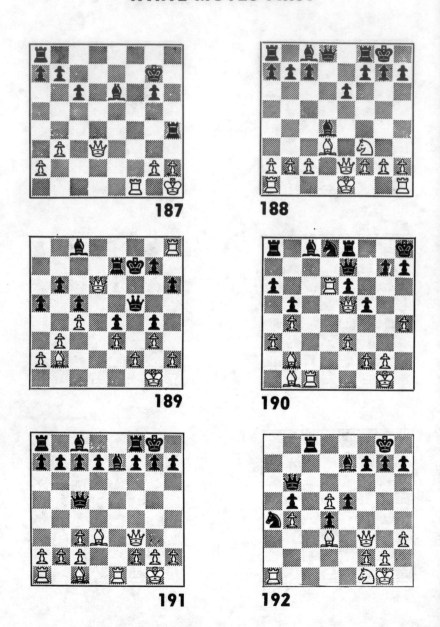

187

188

189

190

191

192

46 · DOUBLE ATTACK ·

193

194

195

196

197

198

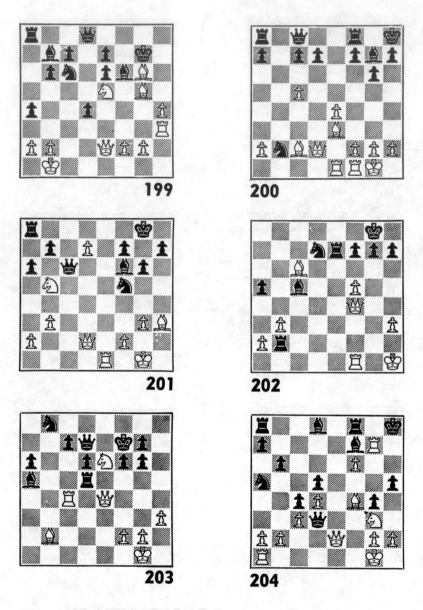

199

200

201

202

203

204

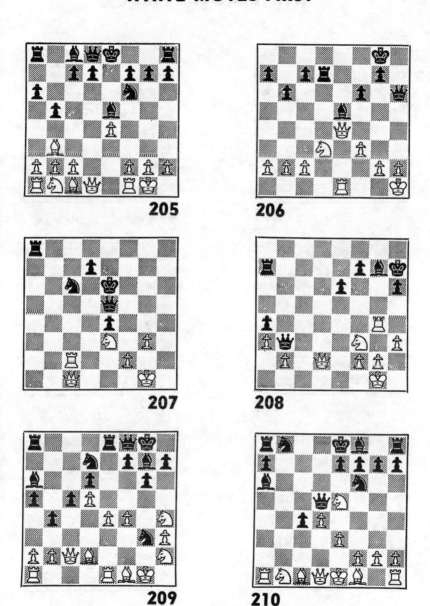

205

206

207

208

209

210

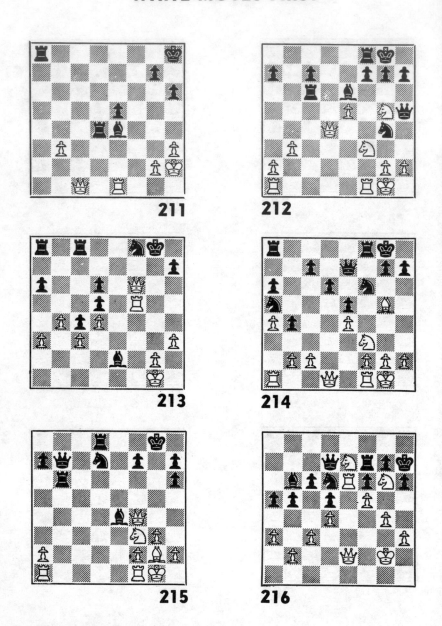

211

212

213

214

215

216

WHITE MOVES FIRST

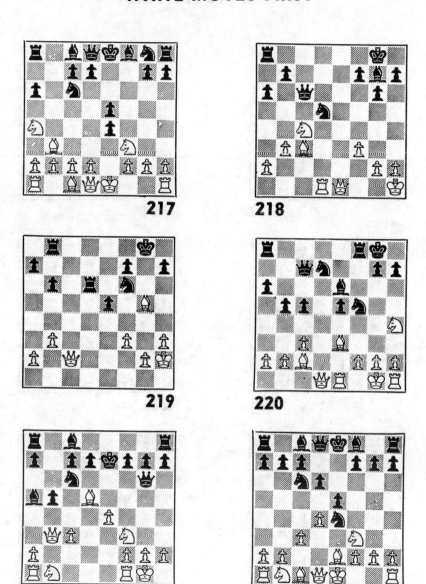

217

218

219

220

221

222

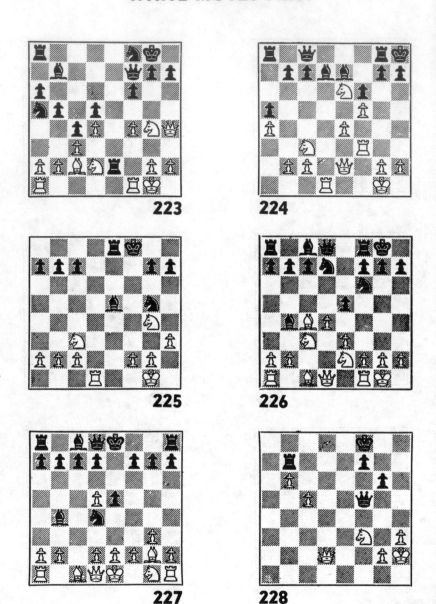

223

224

225

226

227

228

52 · DOUBLE ATTACK ·

WHITE MOVES FIRST

229

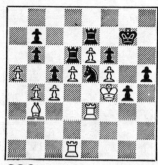

230

231

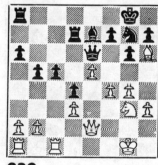

232

233

234

· **DOUBLE ATTACK** · 53

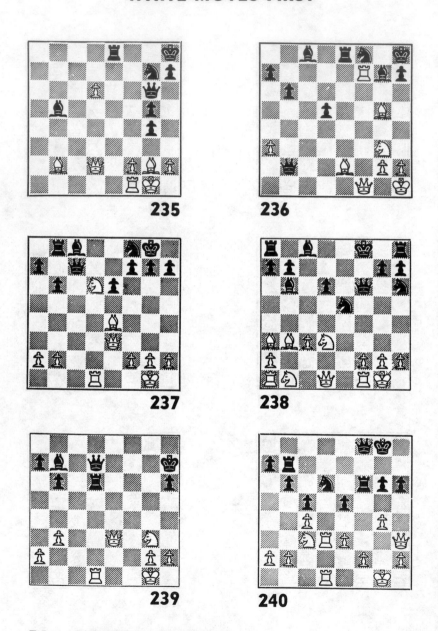

235

236

237

238

239

240

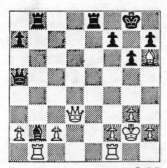

241

242

243

244

245

246

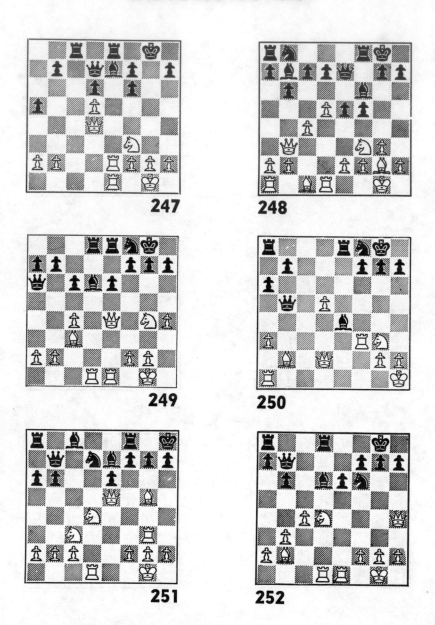

247

248

249

250

251

252

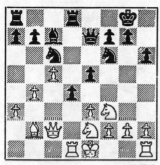

253

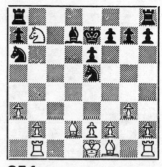

254

255

256

257

258

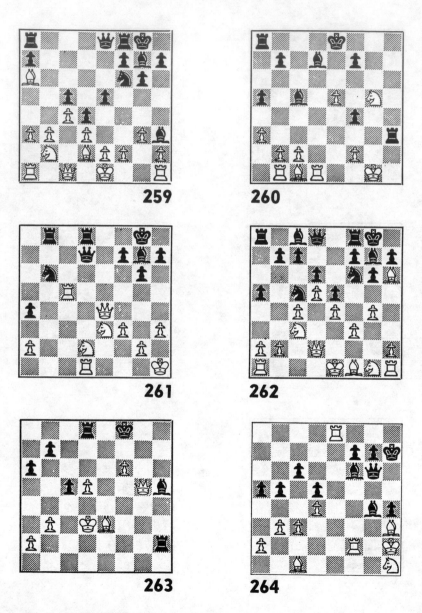

259

260

261

262

263

264

58 · DOUBLE ATTACK ·

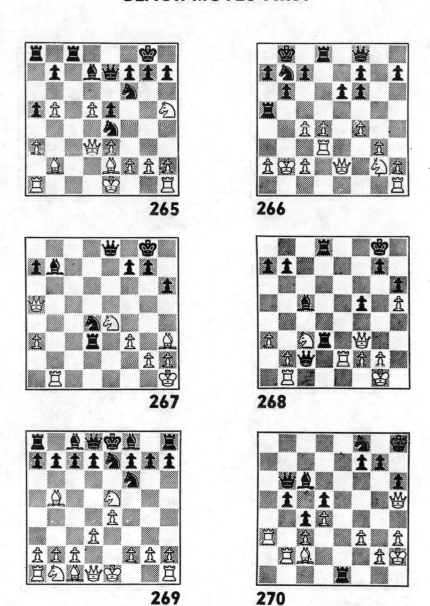

265

266

267

268

269

270

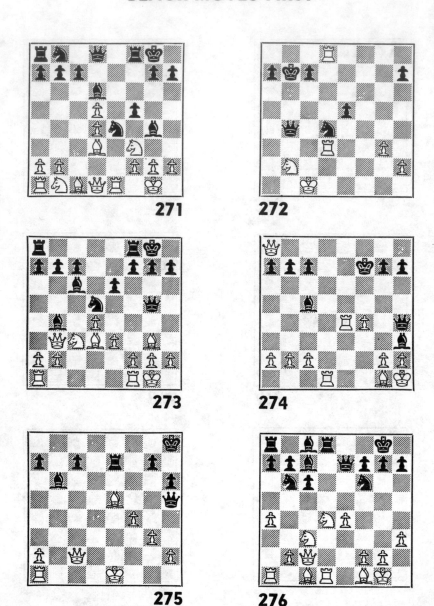

271

272

273

274

275

276

BLACK MOVES FIRST

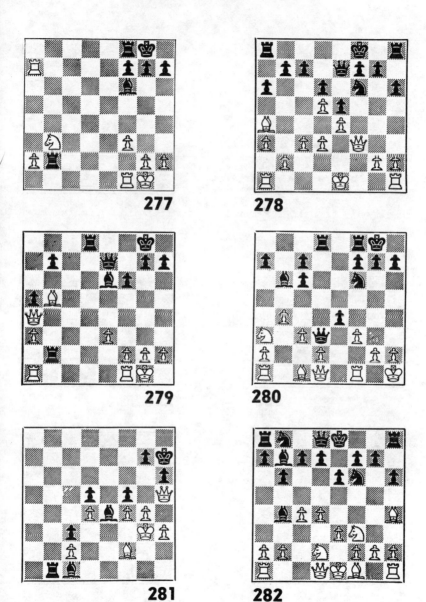

277

278

279

280

281

282

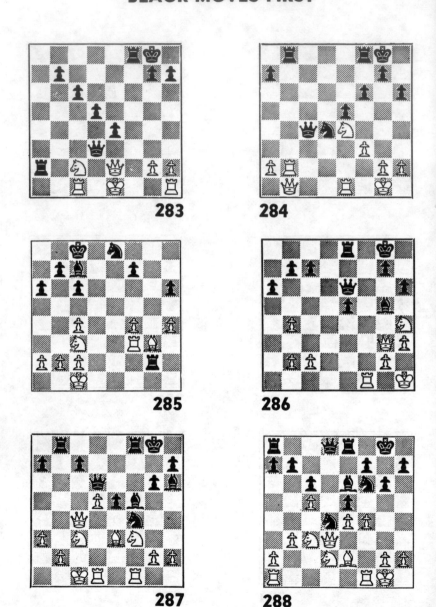

283

284

285

286

287

288

BLACK MOVES FIRST

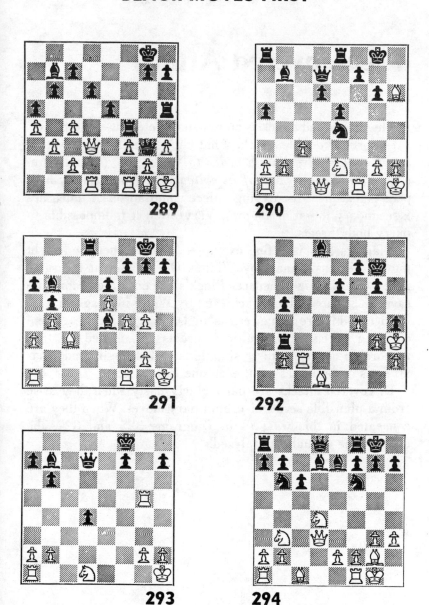

289

290

291

292

293

294

4. Discovered Attack

The discovered attack is an unusually elegant—and powerful—form of double attack. What happens in this case is that *a unit moves off a line in order to "discover"* (actually uncover) *an attack by one of its colleagues.* What usually happens is that the "discovering" piece simultaneously unleashes a secondary threat of its own. Very often it is impossible to parry both threats.

Diagram 295 is a fine example. White's opening Knight move threatens a mate by White's Queen. But at the same time White's Knight menaces Black's Queen, which cannot be saved. The same effect is achieved by White in Diagram 314.

In certain rare instances, as in Diagram 321, we get enchanting effects when multiple threats are opened up. The inexorable beauty of these situations is that the defender has all sorts of resources—but each one fails!

Discovered attacks are particularly nasty when they arise from a plausible series of preliminary moves. When they are concealed in this way, as in Diagrams 325 and 327, the defender is virtually paralyzed.

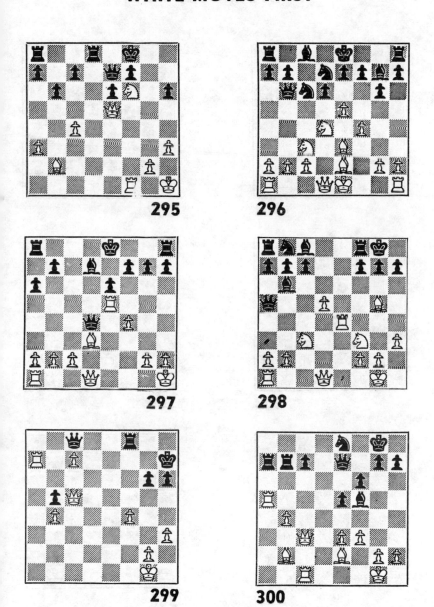

295

296

297

298

299

300

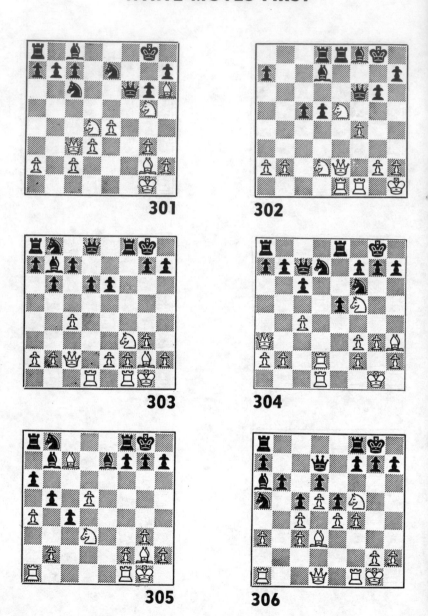

301

302

303

304

305

306

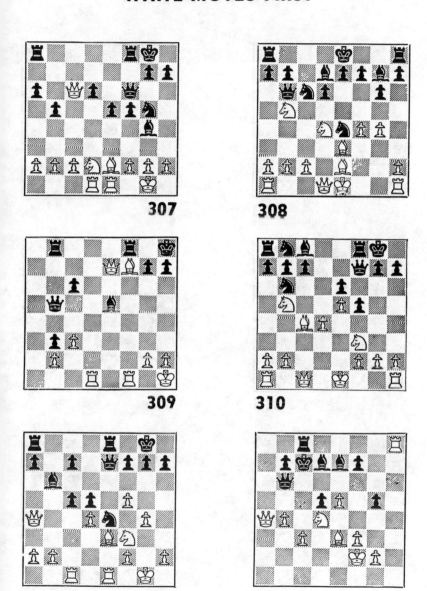

307

308

309

310

311

312

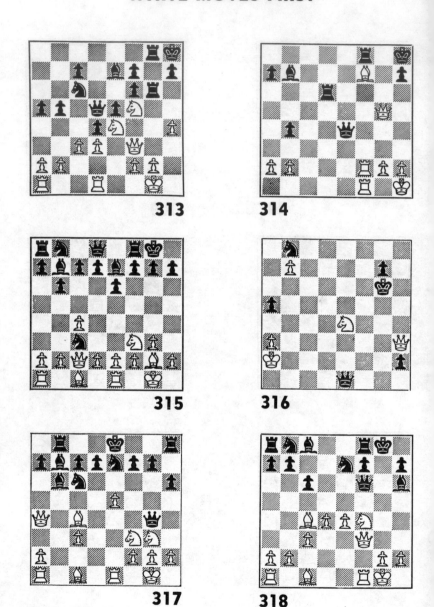

313

314

315

316

317

318

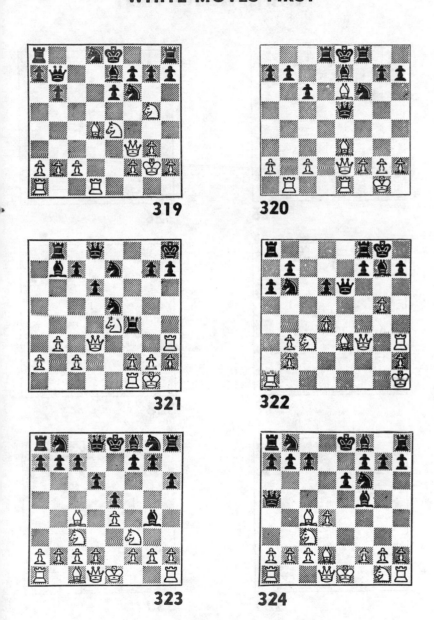

319

320

321

322

323

324

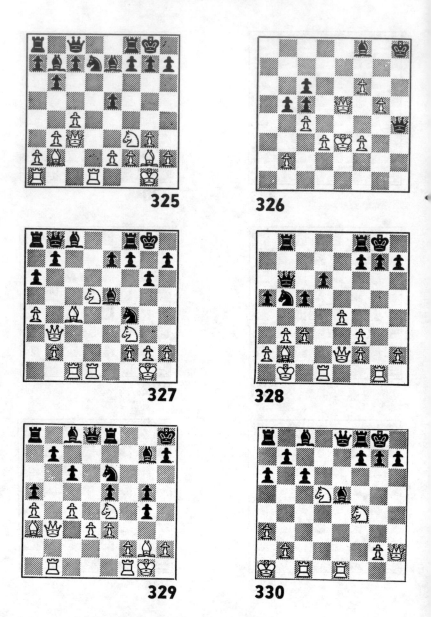

325

326

327

328

329

330

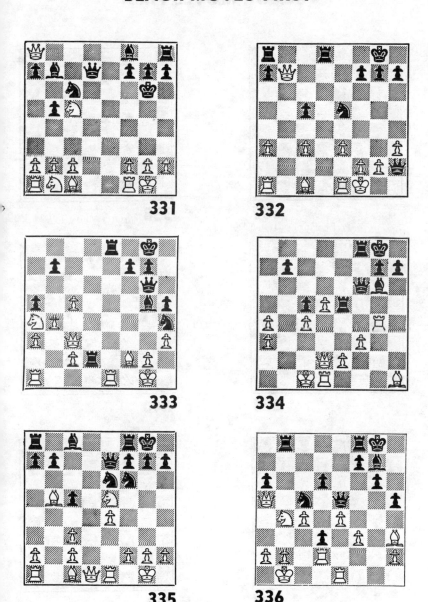

331

332

333

334

335

336

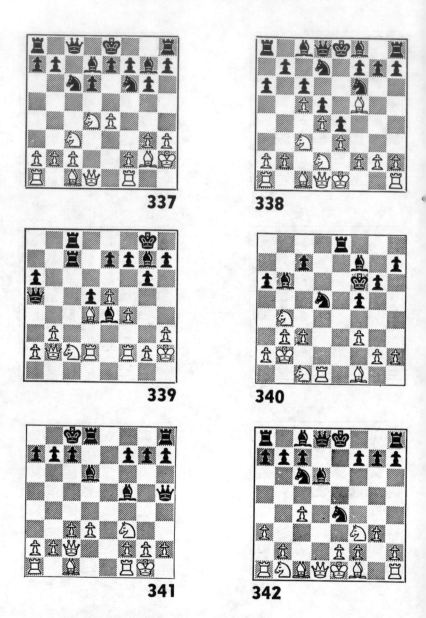

337

338

339

340

341

342

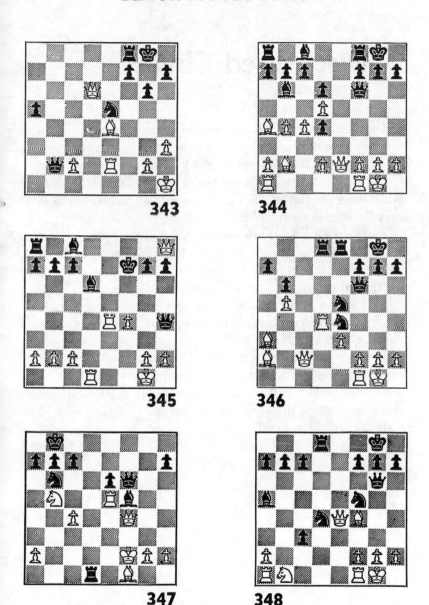

343

344

345

346

347

348

5. Discovered Check

Discovered check is really a kind of discovered attack, with this important difference: *the "discovering" piece moves away to allow its colleague to give check along the vacated line.*

Because of the principle of the priority of check, the hostile King must get out of check. Consequently valuable material may be lost. For example:

In Diagram 366 White moves his Knight from King 4 to give a discovered check with his Rook which is at King 1. The Knight has several possible ways of giving discovered check, but the right move will win Black's Queen.

In Diagram 357 White's first move is so strong that his Rook—the "discovering" piece—cannot be prevented from winning Black's Queen.

Because of this power of the "discovering" piece, it is often possible to make surprising preliminary sacrifices, relying on the power of the coming discovered check to win back much more than the sacrificed material. Diagram 349 illustrates this point very effectively.

WHITE MOVES FIRST

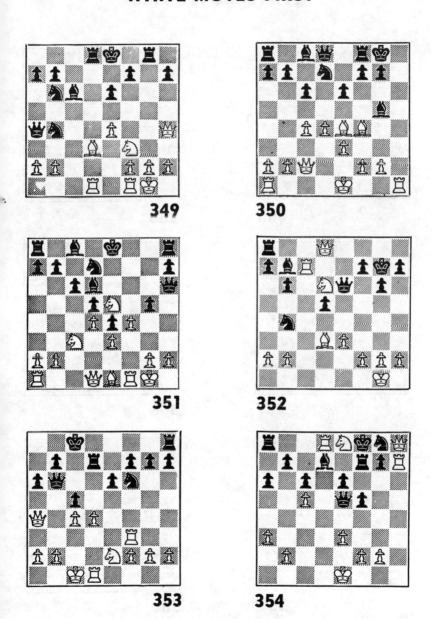

349

350

351

352

353

354

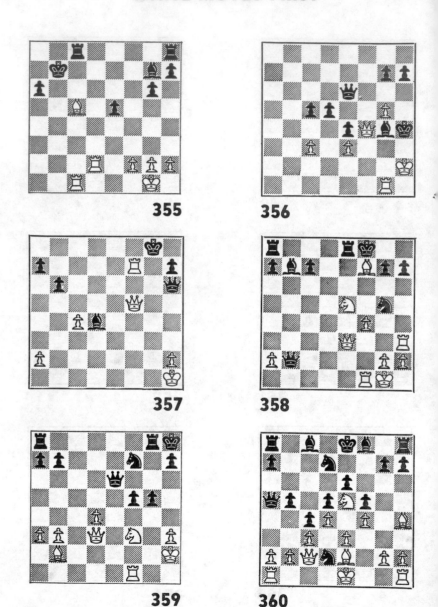

355

356

357

358

359

360

WHITE MOVES FIRST

361

362

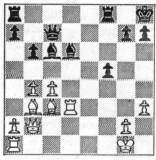

363

364

365

366

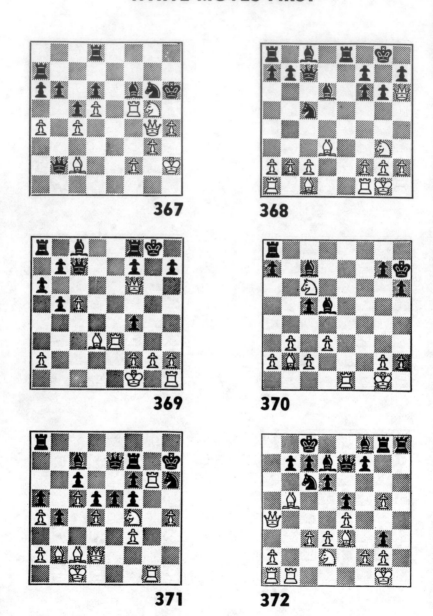

367

368

369

370

371

372

78 · DISCOVERED CHECK ·

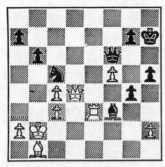

373

374

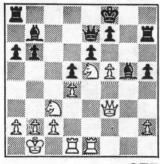

375

376

377

378

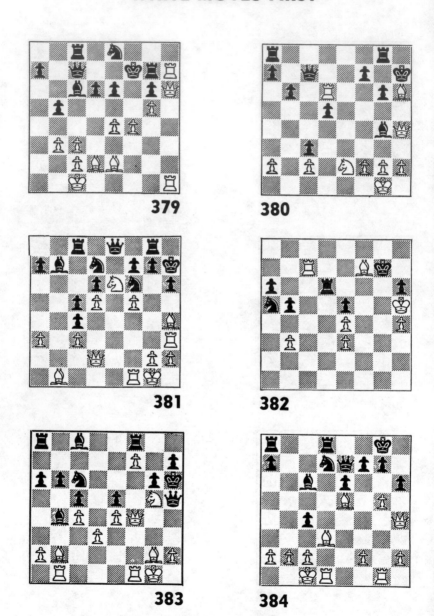

379

380

381

382

383

384

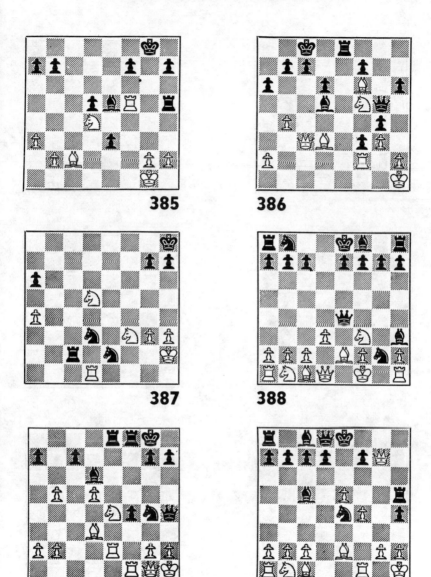

385

386

387

388

389

390

BLACK MOVES FIRST

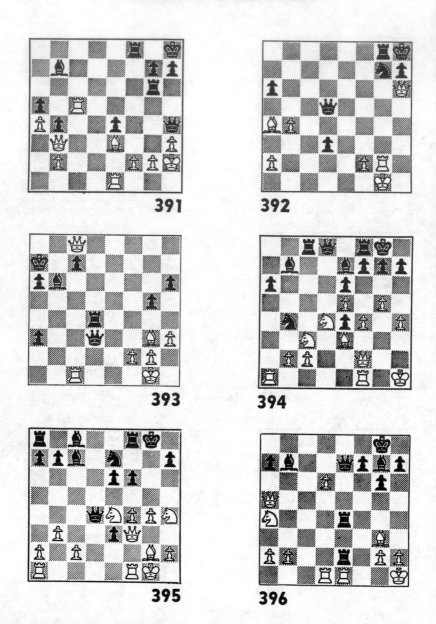

391

392

393

394

395

396

82 · DISCOVERED CHECK ·

6. Double Check

Of all the different kinds of discovered check, the double check is the most dangerous and the most menacing. *For here the "discovering" piece not only uncovers a check; by moving, it gives a direct check.*

This is the most drastic situation that ever confronts a King; for in the case of double check, capture or interposition is impossible. The only way to answer a double check is by moving the King.

Because of its formidable power, the double check has made possible some of the most glamorous combinations in the whole range of chess literature. Diagram 399 is a characteristic example. First comes a completely unexpected Queen sacrifice, followed by a double check with Rook and Bishop, and checkmate next move.

Queen sacrifices are quite common in this section, for the mighty double check easily makes up for the sacrificed material. There are other aritstic possibilities as well, the most beautiful of all appearing in Diagram 407.

Very often the double check brusquely triumphs over hostile attacks, as in the startling finish in Diagram 417. Never underestimate the power of a double check!

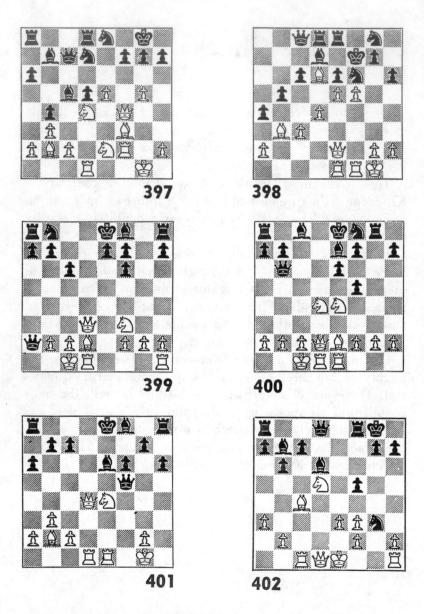

397

398

399

400

401

402

WHITE MOVES FIRST

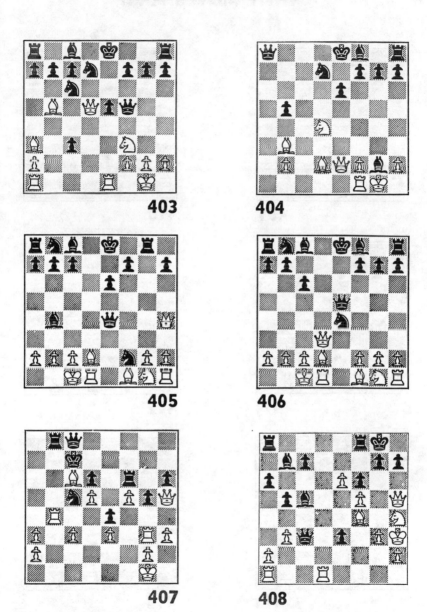

403

404

405

406

407

408

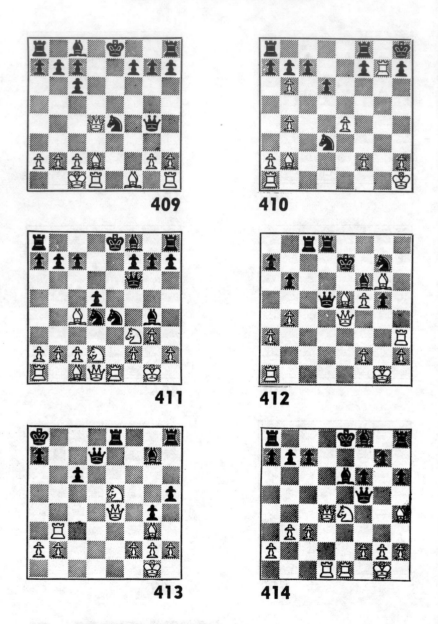

409

410

411

412

413

414

BLACK MOVES FIRST

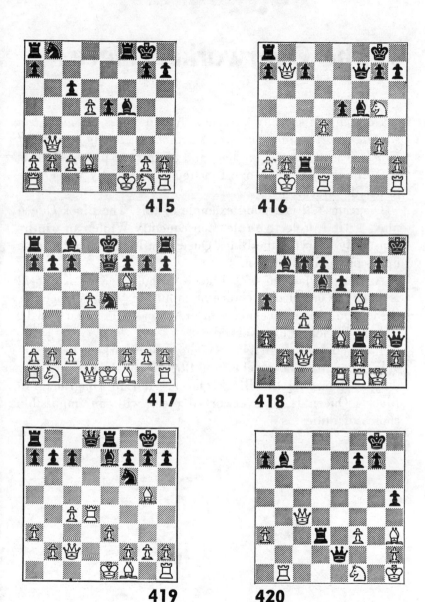

415

416

417

418

419

420

7. The Overworked Piece

No man can serve two masters. And in chess, *no piece can simultaneously guard two pieces without becoming a target of attack.* The principle is clear and simple: a piece which is performing more than one function is especially vulnerable to hostile attack.

Diagram 422 is a good example of this. The Black Queen plays a vital protective role. Consequently White can win by constantly harrying the Black Queen until it is forced to give up its protective function.

Again, in Diagram 430, Black's Bishop at King Knight 2 is given the unwelcome choice of capturing White's Queen or Bishop, allowing checkmate in either case. In other words, Black's Bishop is overworked.

In Diagram 437 Black's Knight is overworked, being unable to capture White's checking Rook because of its primary duty of guarding the Black Queen. And in Diagram 440 Black's Queen is an overworked piece with an impossible choice of duties!

WHITE MOVES FIRST

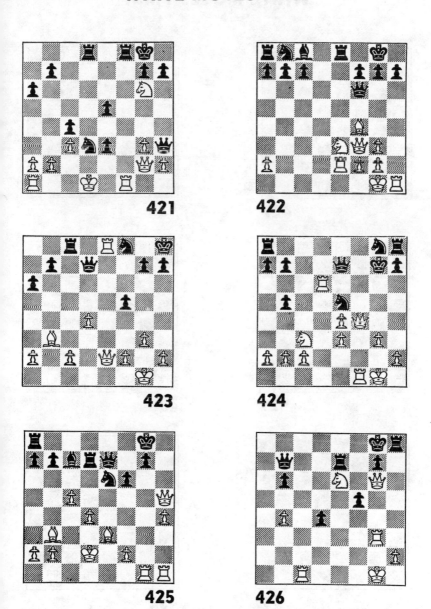

421

422

423

424

425

426

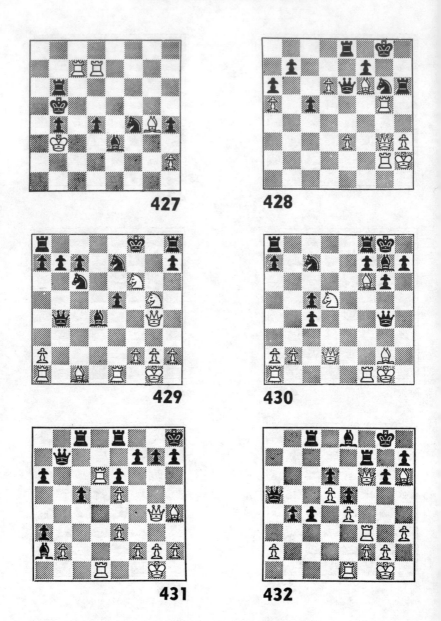

427

428

429

430

431

432

90 · The OVERWORKED PIECE ·

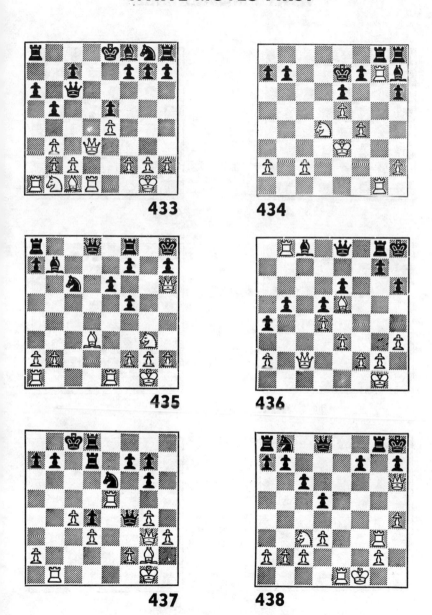

433

434

435

436

437

438

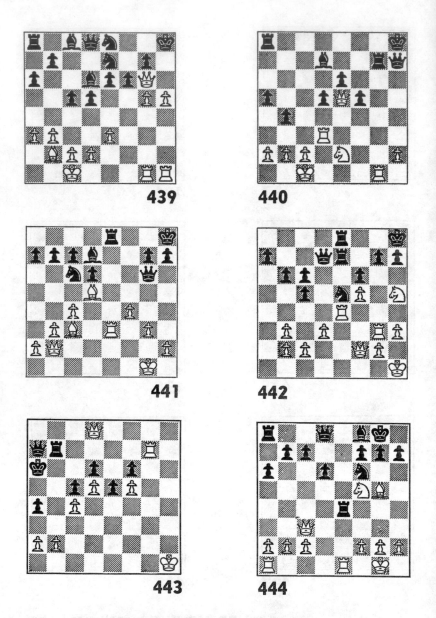

439

440

441

442

443

444

92 · The OVERWORKED PIECE ·

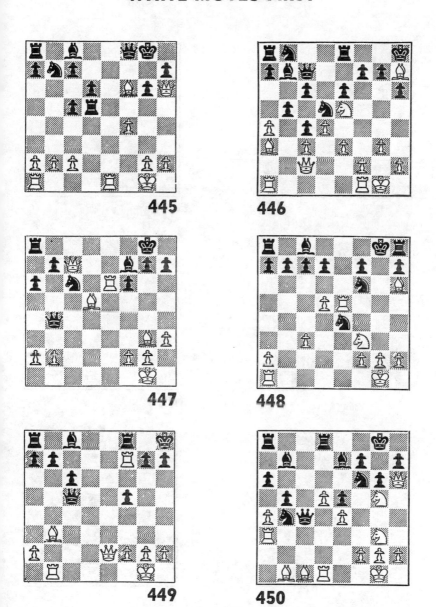

445

446

447

448

449

450

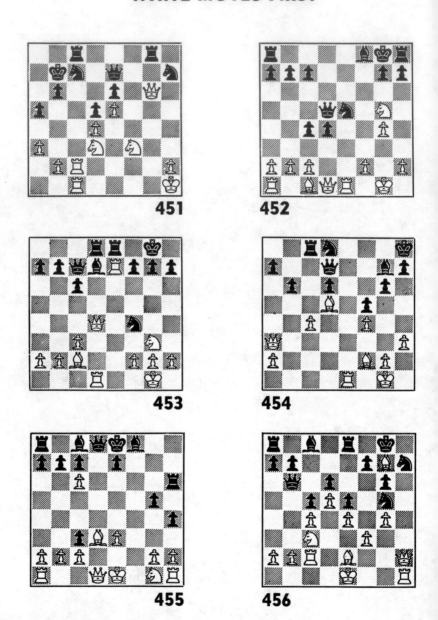

451

452

453

454

455

456

BLACK MOVES FIRST

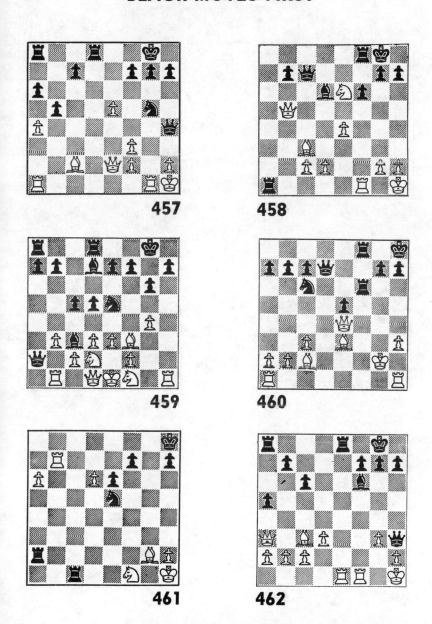

457

458

459

460

461

462

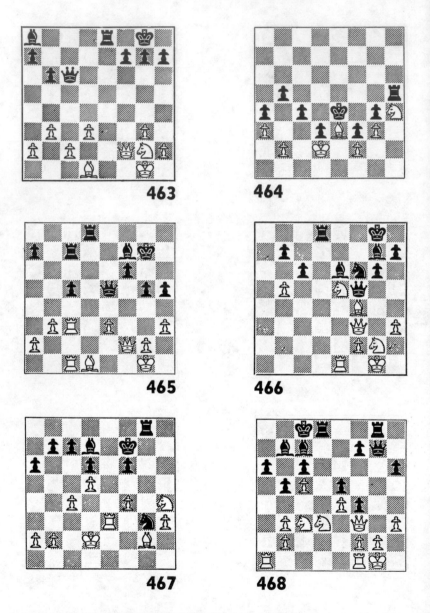

463

464

465

466

467

468

BLACK MOVES FIRST

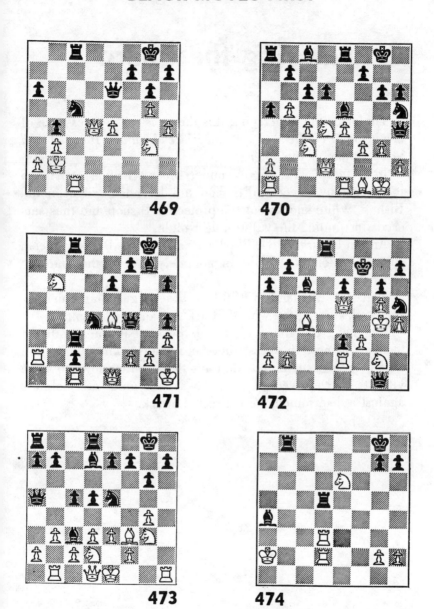

469

470

471

472

473

474

8. Removing the Guard

The principle underlying this theme is the very essence of chess logic. *If Piece A guards Piece B, attack Piece A and you win one or the other.*

In Diagram 477, for example, Black's Knight at King 5 is attacked by Queen and Bishop and defended by Queen and Bishop. White knocks out the protective Bishop and thus succeeds in winning the vulnerable Knight.

And in Diagram 484, Black's Rook protects Black's Queen. But not for long, for White immediately removes the guardian Rook.

Note also in Diagram 486 how Black's guardian Queen is removed, forcing the win of Black's unguarded Rook.

Removing the guard is one of the most useful of all the tactical themes. In chess, there is no surer winning method than concentrating on hostile units that are tied down to some vital task. Deprived of mobility, these units are helpless against a determined, well directed attack.

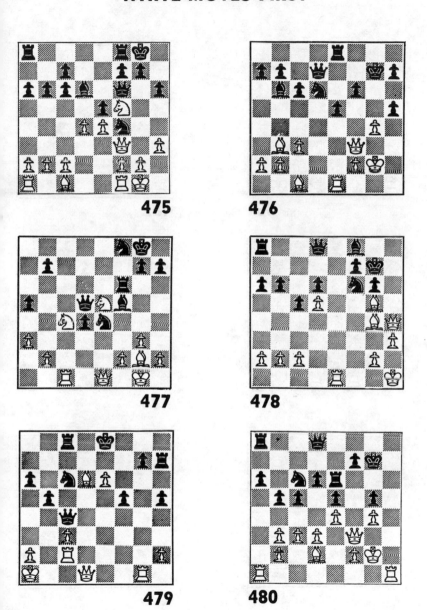

475

476

477

478

479

480

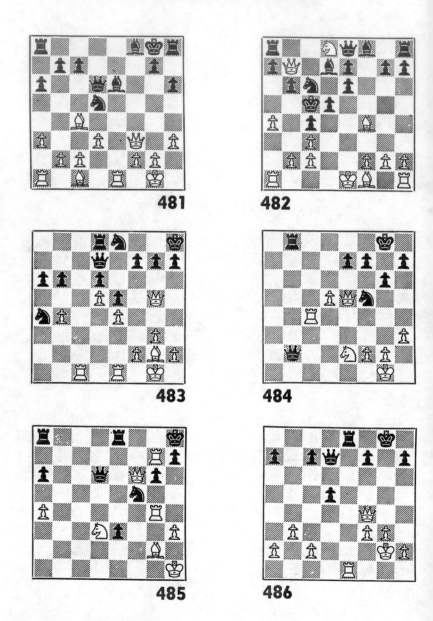

481

482

483

484

485

486

100 · **REMOVING** the **GUARD** ·

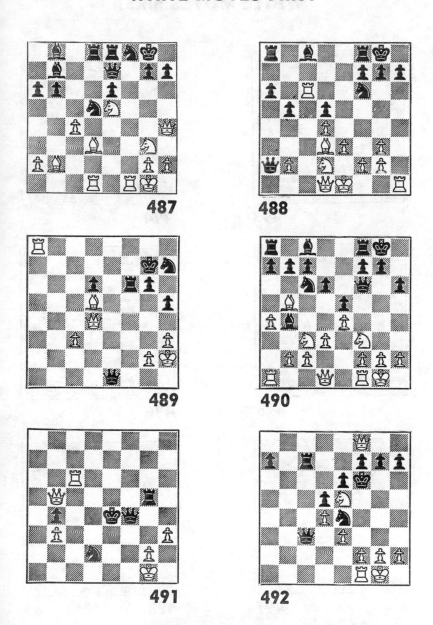

487

488

489

490

491

492

WHITE MOVES FIRST

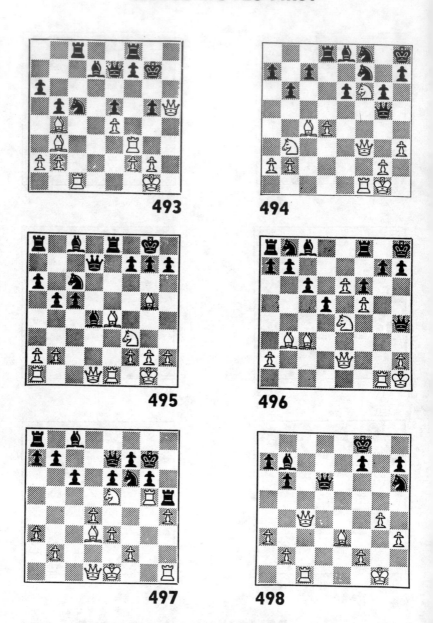

493

494

495

496

497

498

102 · REMOVING the GUARD ·

WHITE MOVES FIRST

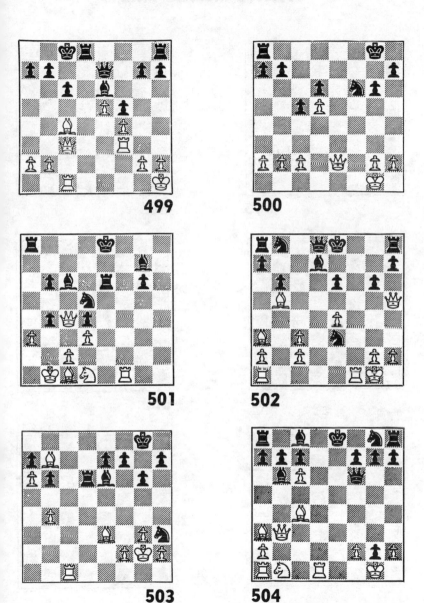

499

500

501

502

503

504

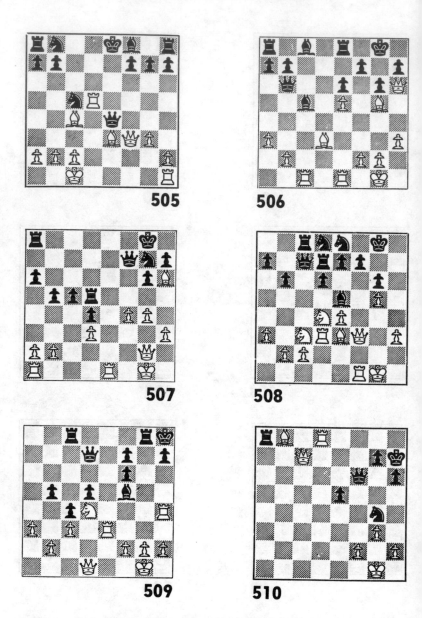

505

506

507

508

509

510

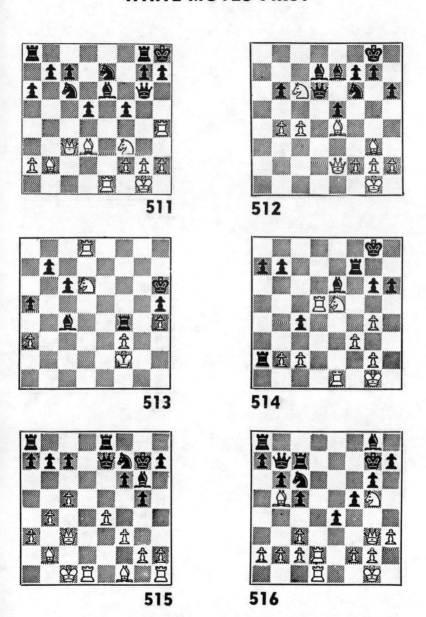

511

512

513

514

515

516

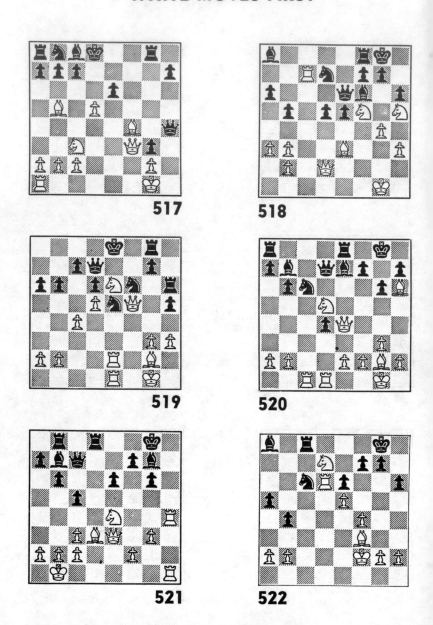

517

518

519

520

521

522

BLACK MOVES FIRST

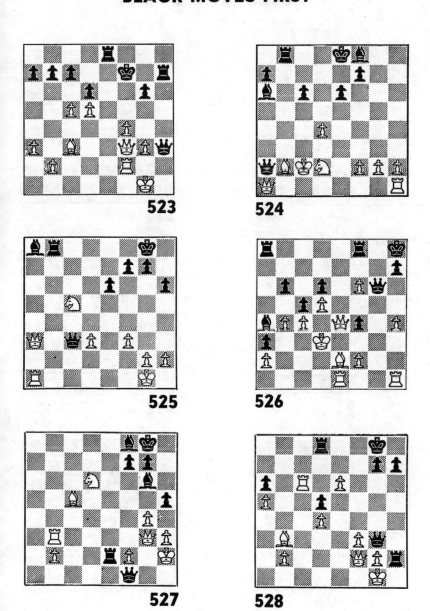

523

524

525

526

527

528

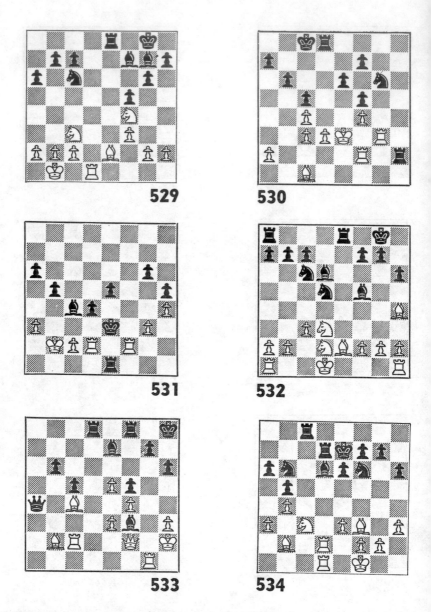

529

530

531

532

533

534

BLACK MOVES FIRST

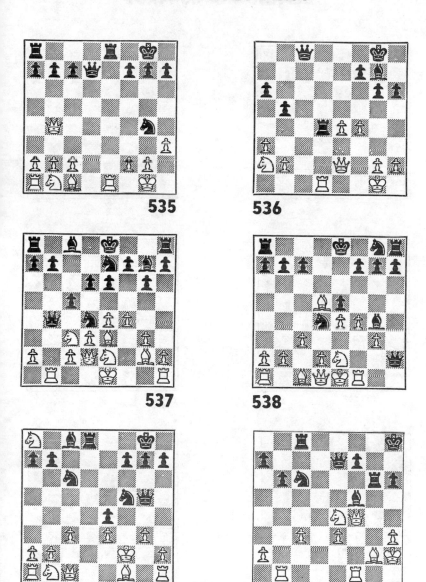

535

536

537

538

539

540

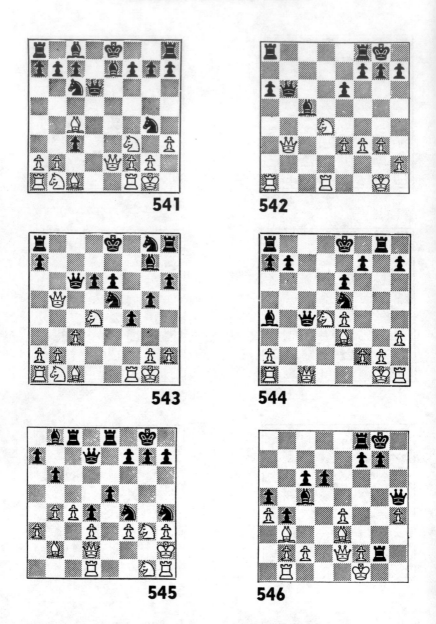

541

542

543

544

545

546

110 · REMOVING the GUARD ·

9. Clearance

Clearance is the term we use to describe *the removal of a piece from a square in order to make that square available to another unit.* Often this occupation by the new piece involves a decisive attack, hence we clear the square even if it involves a spectacular sacrifice of material.

In Diagram 547, for example, White clears the square King 5 by sacrificing his Knight. But the Knight move looks senseless, and it is followed by a Queen sacrifice that looks more spectacular and even more senseless. However, there follows a terrific double check and Black cannot escape checkmate! Then all the moves of the combination appear in their proper perspective, and we see that the initial clearance move was really a stroke of genius. Observe, by the way, that this clearance move involved an attack on Black's Queen and thus left him no time to rearrange his forces for adequate defense.

In Diagram 549 White's clearance maneuver depends on a check, which, because of its imperious nature, allows Black no time to prevent White's Pawn from queening.

In general, you will note that a good clearance move is apt to be peremptory. The point is that the defender is given no time to parry the threat that is the real point of the clearance move.

547

548

549

550

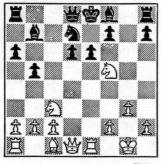

551

552

WHITE MOVES FIRST

553

554

555

556

557

558

WHITE MOVES FIRST

559

560

561

562

563

564

WHITE MOVES FIRST

565

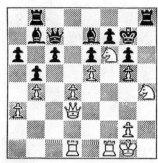

566

567

568

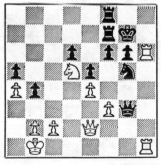

569

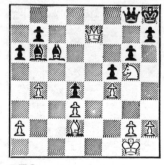

570

571

572

573

574

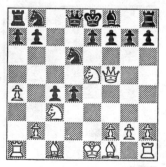

575

576

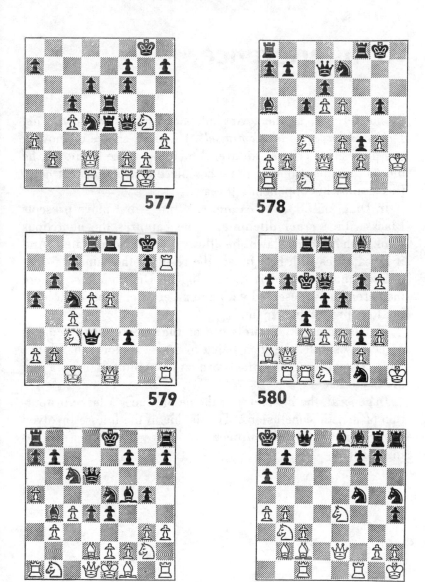

577

578

579

580

581

582

10. Interference

Interference, as the term indicates, occurs where *the defender is forced to block himself*. He has a choice of moving two pieces to a critical square. Whichever piece he moves, he blocks the operations of the other piece and is thus left helpless against his opponent's threats.

In Diagram 583, for example, White's first move presents Black with a cruel dilemma. If he captures the obnoxious Rook with his King Pawn, he allows himself to be mated. And if he captures with his Queen, the result is the same.

Even more artistic is the setting of Diagram 604, where the defender is presented with a number of choices, each leading to a pretty checkmate.

In Diagram 606 White's use of the interference theme is especially subtle, the idea being to create a block on White's King 5 square so that Black cannot save himself by playing ... Q—B4ch.

In general, the interference theme produces a large proportion of artistic conclusions. This is due to the finesse involved in forcing the defender's pieces to destroy each other's working ability.

583

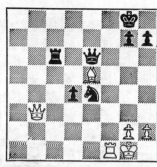

584

585

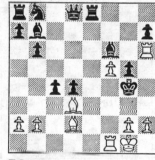

586

587

588

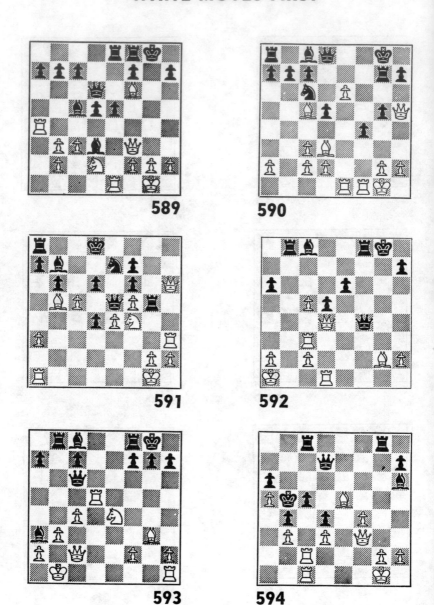

589

590

591

592

593

594

WHITE MOVES FIRST

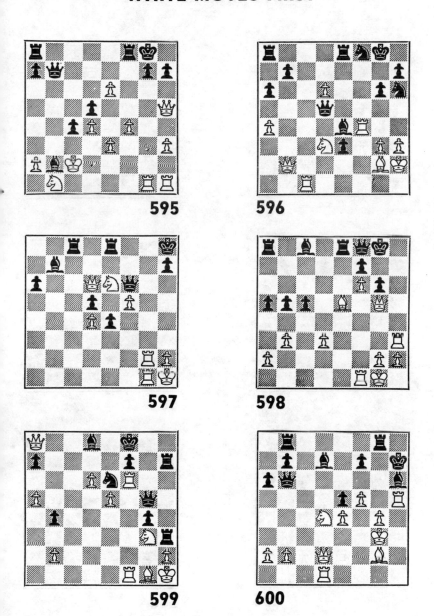

595

596

597

598

599

600

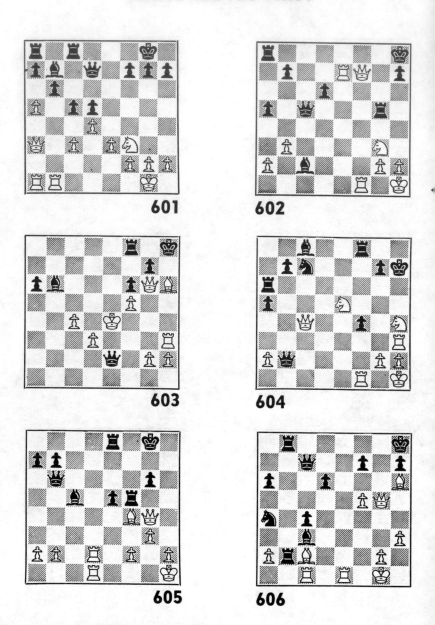

601

602

603

604

605

606

BLACK MOVES FIRST

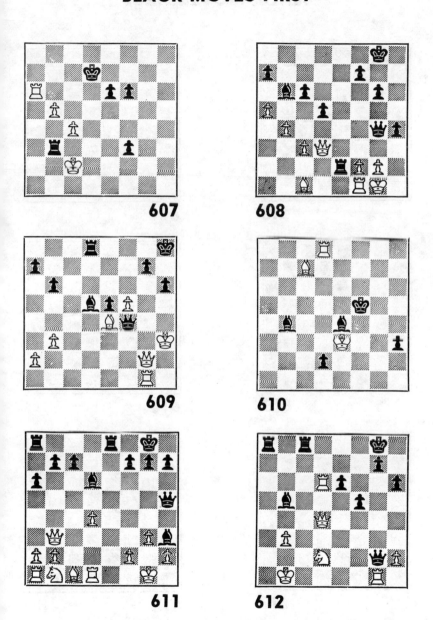

607

608

609

610

611

612

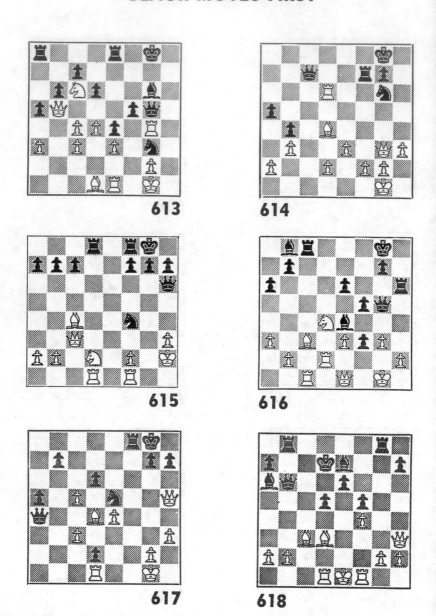

613

614

615

616

617

618

BLACK MOVES FIRST

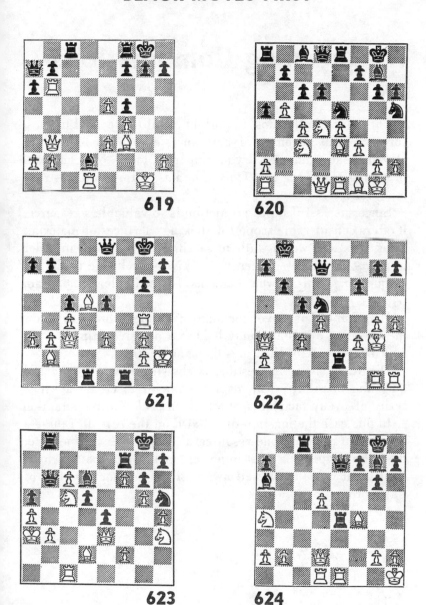

619

620

621

622

623

624

II. Queening Combinations

This is one of the most important of all the tactical themes, for successful queening of a Pawn is equivalent to being a Queen ahead. And even if your opponent loses "only" a piece in gevving rid of the new Queen, he has suffered a disastrous material loss.

Since successful Pawn promotion is so valuable a resource, it offers considerable scope for striking sacrifices of material. Thus, it is well worth while to sacrifice one's Queen in order to promote to a new Queen which gives checkmate in the act of queening. This is what happens, for example, in Diagram 645.

Diagram 631 is one of the many examples which show how the queening of a Pawn may lead to a decisive gain of material. Diagram 625 illustrates the same motif.

Diagram 648 is interesting as showing how the potential queening possibility can inspire a player to create a whole series of pretty tactical strokes. Given a *clue* to the situation —in this case the location of a Pawn on the seventh rank—a player can think up one resourceful move after another. But the initial impetus is most important of all, and that is why it is of great value to be well aware of the enormous power of Pawn promotion.

WHITE MOVES FIRST

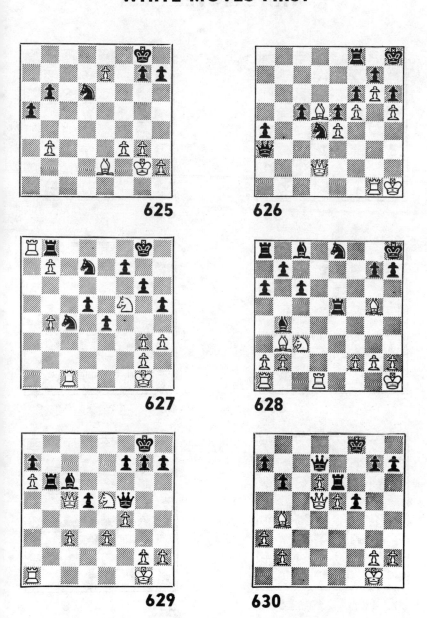

625

626

627

628

629

630

· QUEENING COMBINATIONS · 127

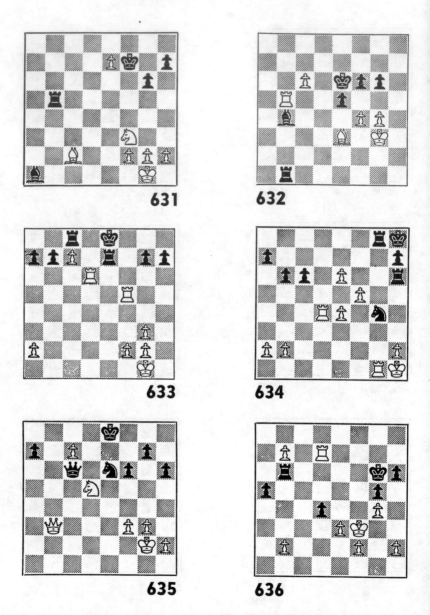

631

632

633

634

635

636

WHITE MOVES FIRST

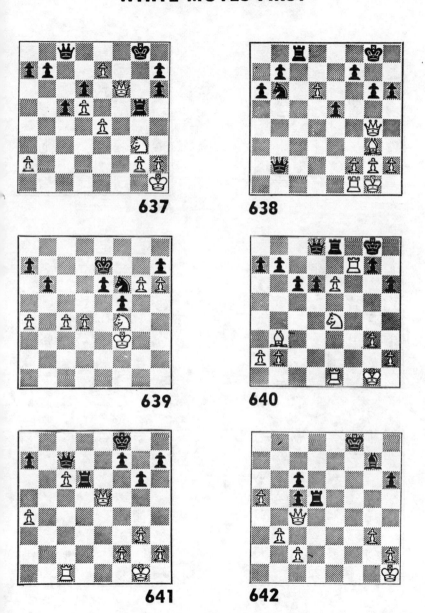

637

638

639

640

641

642

WHITE MOVES FIRST

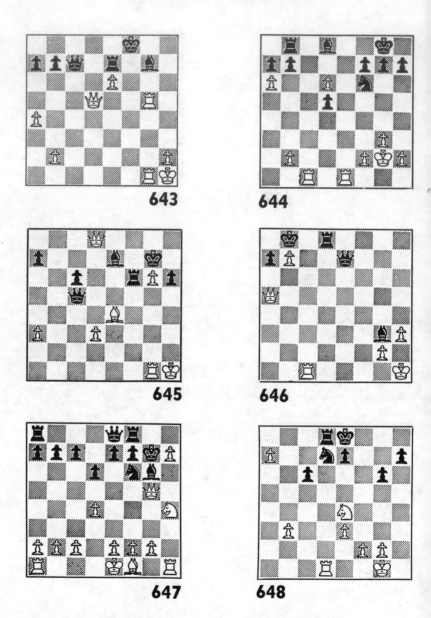

643

644

645

646

647

648

BLACK MOVES FIRST

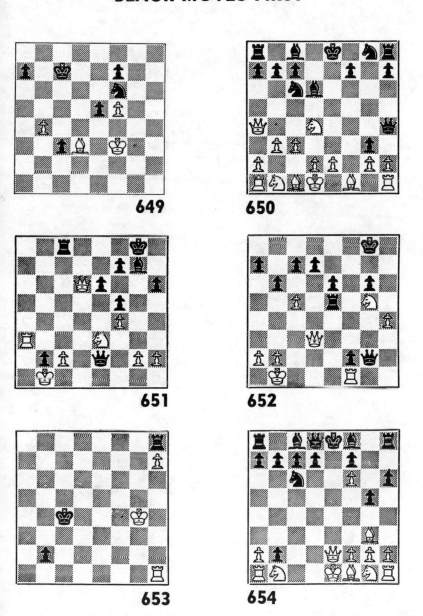

649

650

651

652

653

654

· QUEENING COMBINATIONS · 131

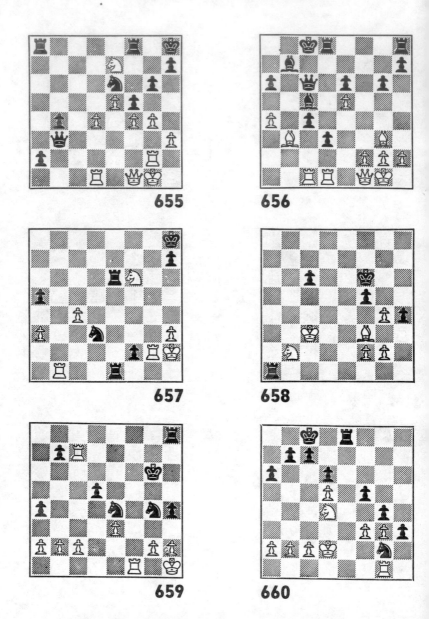

655

656

657

658

659

660

BLACK MOVES FIRST

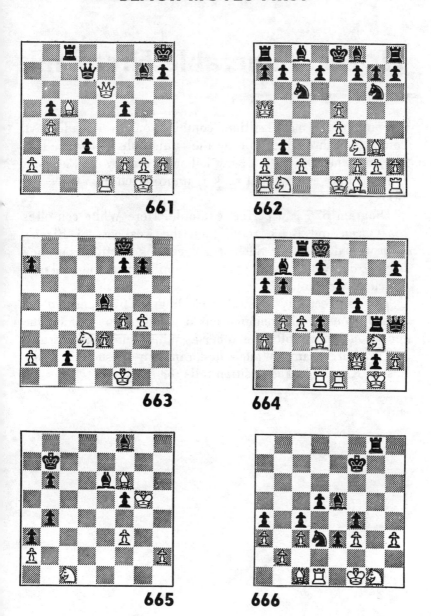

661

662

663

664

665

666

12. The Vulnerable First Rank

Some of the most brilliant combinations ever made have come about through exploiting the vulnerable first rank. This happens when the castled King is hemmed in by the Pawns in front of him, and his first rank is unprotected by a Queen or Rook.

Diagram 676 is a perfect example. Here White can offer his Queen and Rook, relying on the weakness of Black's unprotected first rank. Such sacrifices look startling, but they become quite obvious once you are familiar with the weakness which they exploit.

This is effectively illustrated in Diagram 679, perhaps the most famous of all combinations devoted to this theme. One sensational move follows another as White relies on his crushing pressure against White's first rank. In all such cases the hostile King's blocked position tells the story.

WHITE MOVES FIRST

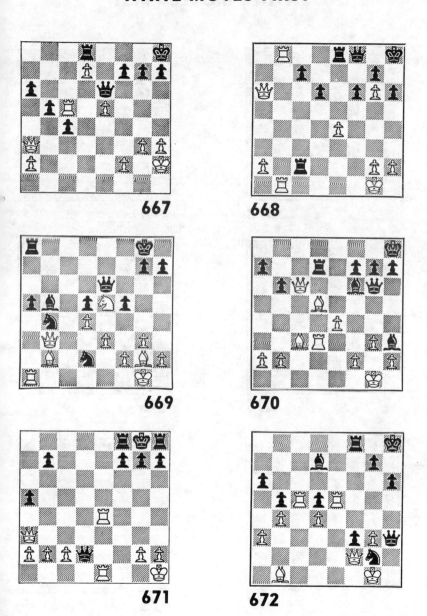

667

668

669

670

671

672

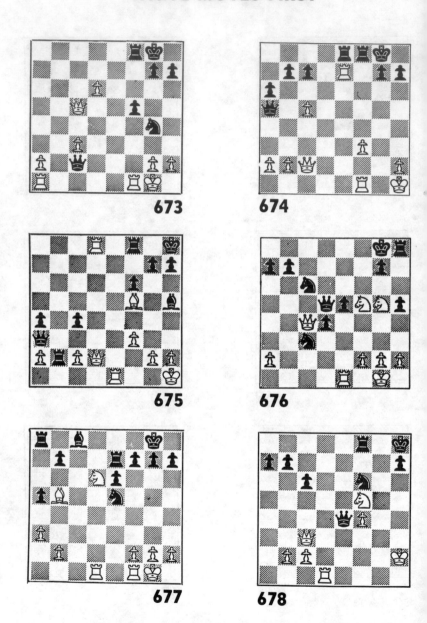

673

674

675

676

677

678

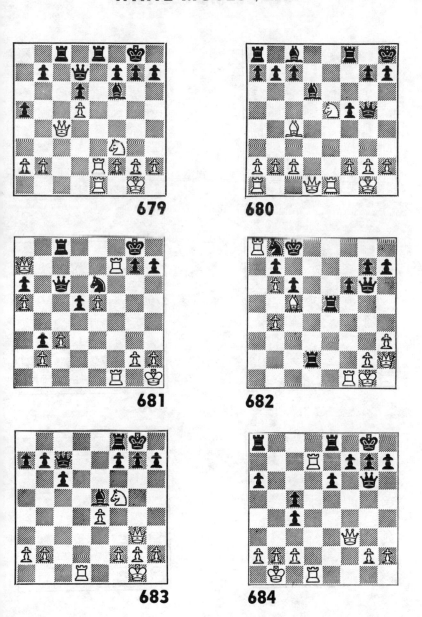

679

680

681

682

683

684

BLACK MOVES FIRST

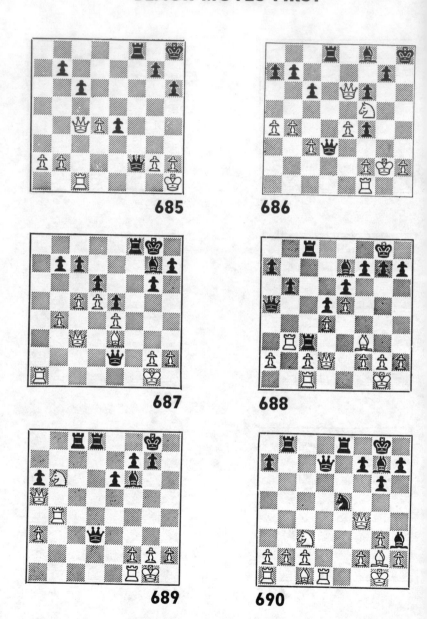

685

686

687

688

689

690

138 · The VULNERABLE FIRST RANK ·

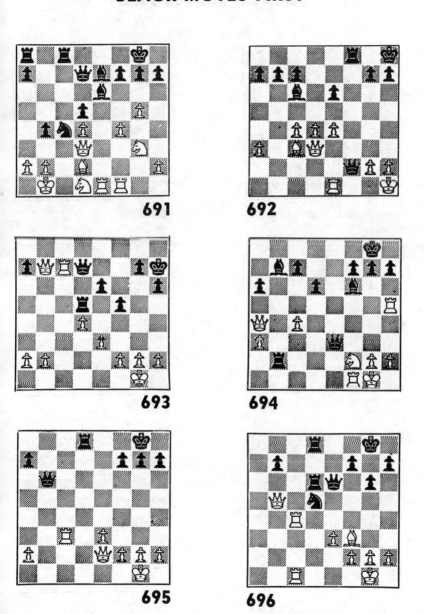

691

692

693

694

695

696

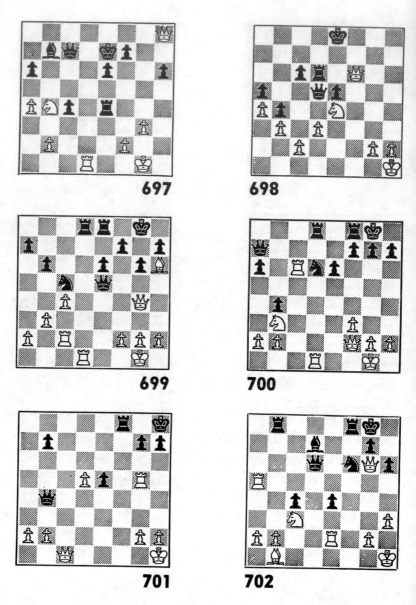

697

698

699

700

701

702

13. Queen Sacrifices

No matter how experienced and sophisticated a chessplayer may be, he is always thrilled by a Queen sacrifice. This is understandable, for the Queen is far and away the strongest of all the chess forces.

Precisely because the Queen is so powerful, the sacrifice of this piece must necessarily bring in substantial returns. Mate is usually the sequel, as for example in Diagram 703, where White offers the Queen in a manner which is surprising but hardly generous. He threatens mate, and when the Queen is captured, he mates just the same. Still, such a sacrifice deserves our praise, for it takes real imagination to see the possibilities in such a position.

What is even more admirable is a Queen sacrifice which leads to a fairly long-winded mate. In Diagram 708, for example, White's Queen sacrifice looks like a typographical error. Who would dream that after the Queen sacrifice White has a forced mate in five moves, making use of Rooks and minor pieces—and even a "lowly" Pawn that draws the Black King into a mating net.

Perhaps even more striking are those Queen sacrifices which are followed up by a series of inspired moves—all with the purpose of winning a . . . mere Pawn! Diagram 734 shows such a combination, which was rightly awarded a First Brilliancy Prize.

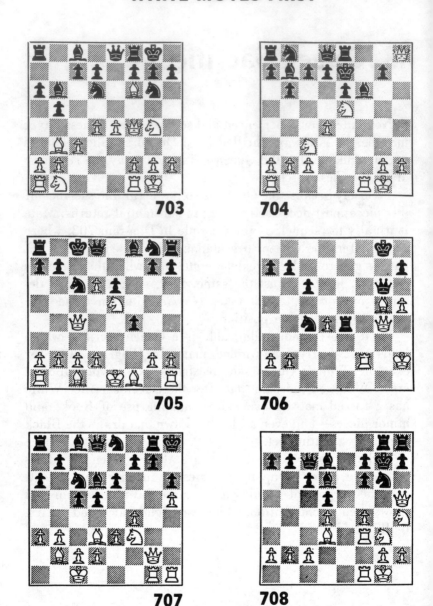

703

704

705

706

707

708

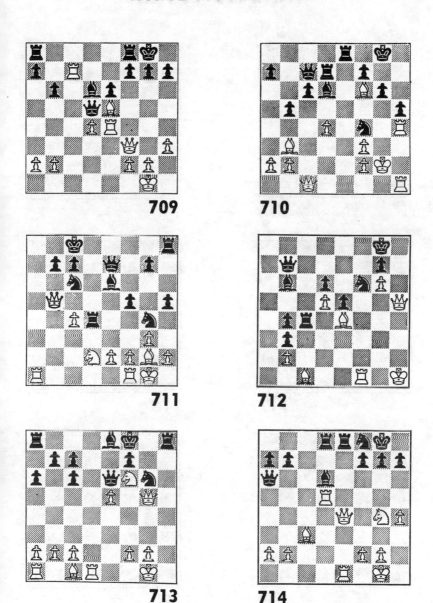

709

710

711

712

713

714

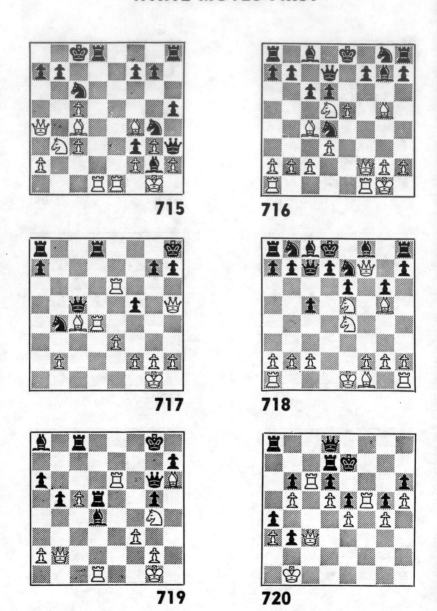

715

716

717

718

719

720

721

722

723

724

725

726

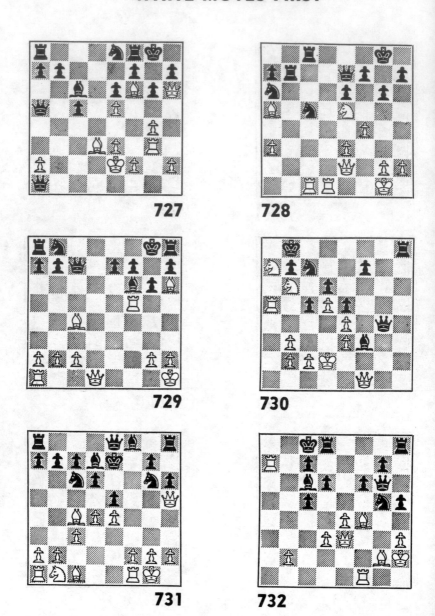

727

728

729

730

731

732

733

734

735

736

737

738

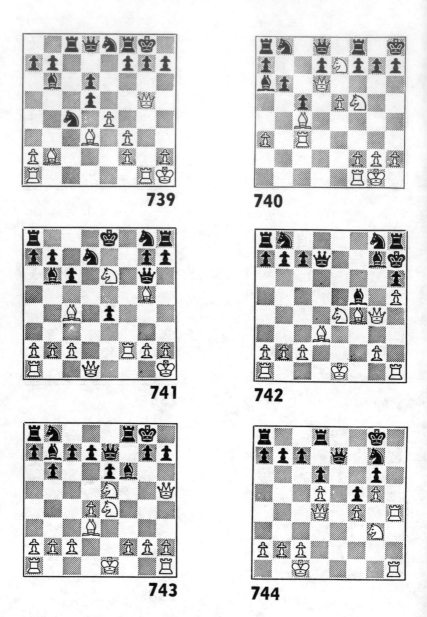

739

740

741

742

743

744

BLACK MOVES FIRST

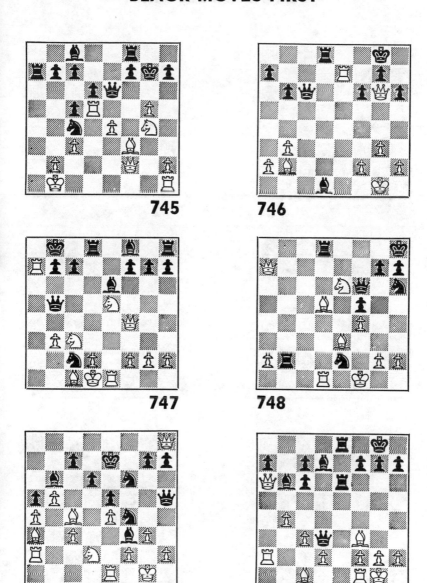

745

746

747

748

749

750

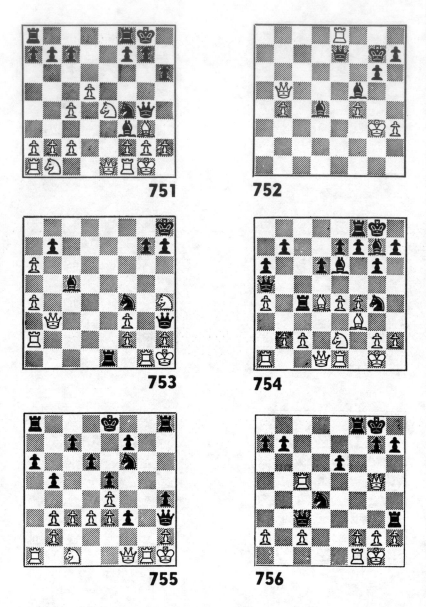

751

752

753

754

755

756

14. X-Ray Attack

The X-ray attack, or skewer attack, is the opposite of the pin. In the X-ray attack, *a piece attacks a hostile piece which is situated on a line with another piece of lesser value*. When the attacked piece moves off the line, it exposes the second piece to capture.

This concept may sound complicated, but an example will show its simplicity—and deadly effectiveness. In Diagram 757 White's Rook maneuvers the Black forces into an X-ray position. Thereupon White's Rook X-rays the Black King, and thus wins the Black Rook.

In Diagram 759 White sets up an X-ray position by sacrificing the Exchange as a preliminary to X-raying the Black King and thereby winning the Black Queen.

Diagram 769 illustrates what is perhaps the most beautiful of all X-ray combinations. Here White sacrifices both Rooks in order to carry out a series of X-ray threats which wind up with the win of Black's Queen. And this comes just in the nick of time, as Black is on the point of administering checkmate!

As explained in the first paragraph, the piece initially menaced by the X-ray is the more important piece. Usually, therefore, the X-ray move is a check (an attack on the King). However, the X-ray may menace other pieces as well. In Diagram 773, for example, White X-rays the Queen in order to win a Rook.

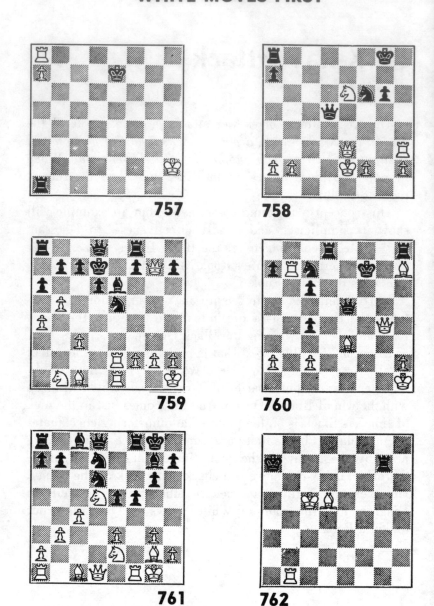

757

758

759

760

761

762

152 · X-RAY ATTACK ·

WHITE MOVES FIRST

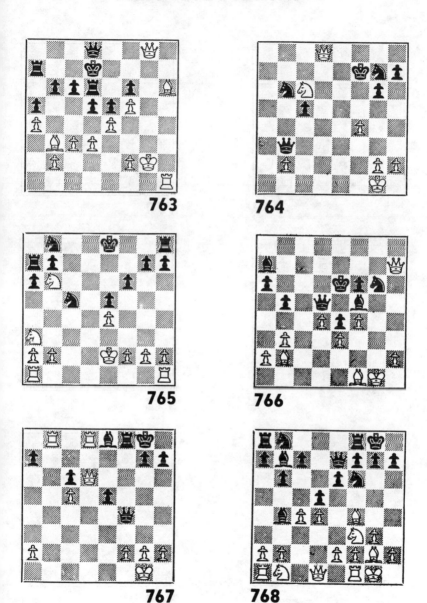

763

764

765

766

767

768

769

770

771

772

773

774

BLACK MOVES FIRST

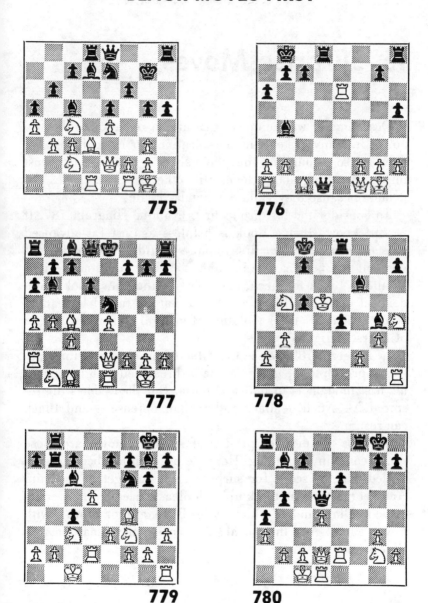

775

776

777

778

779

780

15. Surprise Moves

Occasionally we see moves that are so remarkable they do not fit into any systematic classification. Or even if they do, they are so astounding that their surprise value is the most impressive thing about them. Still other surprise moves are notable because they violate a standard rule!

To consider the last group first, examine Diagram 787. It is well known that a Rook is helpless against far-advanced passed Pawns, and our first impulse would be to dismiss this position as a perfect case in point. Yet White does not resign; he allows Black to queen, and then sacrifices his Rook! Suddenly it turns out that White has a mate in three! Instead of being dismayed at this violation of general principles, we are of course delighted.

In Diagram 789 we see the value of an alert and imaginative approach to the game. White is threatened with mate, and his first thought is to find a defense. But then comes the inspired N—N6ch!—attack rather than defense!—and Black can resign.

Perhaps the most surprising of surprise moves are those which come in the ending. Here the position has been so simplified that the scope for surprise seems altogether too thin. And yet masters can think up such pleasantries as the opening move in Diagram 817 which leaves Black a Rook down—with a won game! And the moral? A surprise move may be possible in *any* position.

WHITE MOVES FIRST

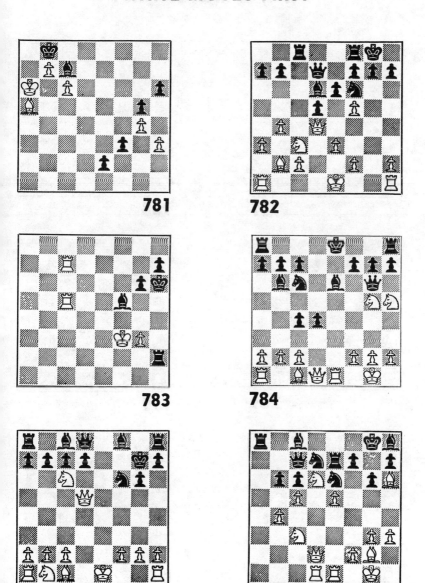

781

782

783

784

785

786

WHITE MOVES FIRST

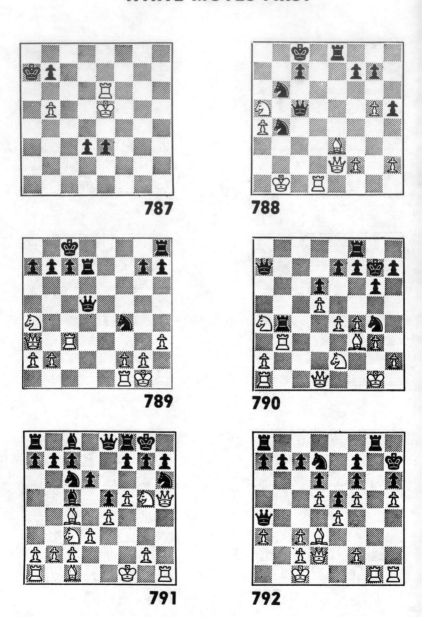

787

788

789

790

791

792

WHITE MOVES FIRST

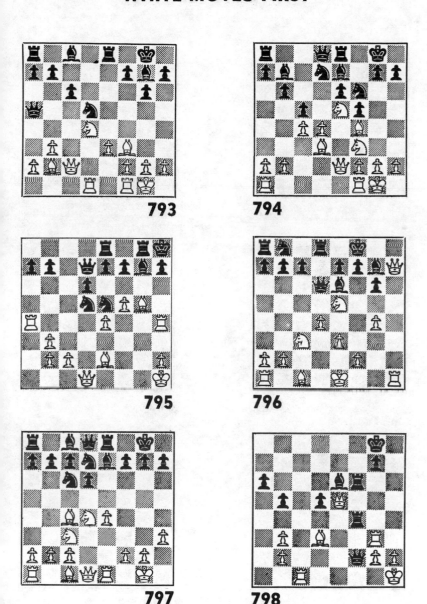

793

794

795

796

797

798

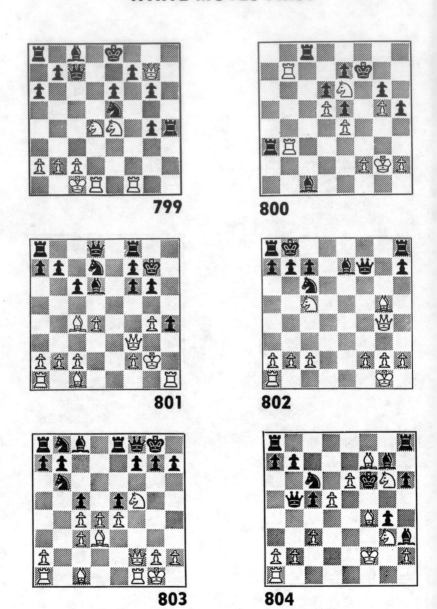

799

800

801

802

803

804

BLACK MOVES FIRST

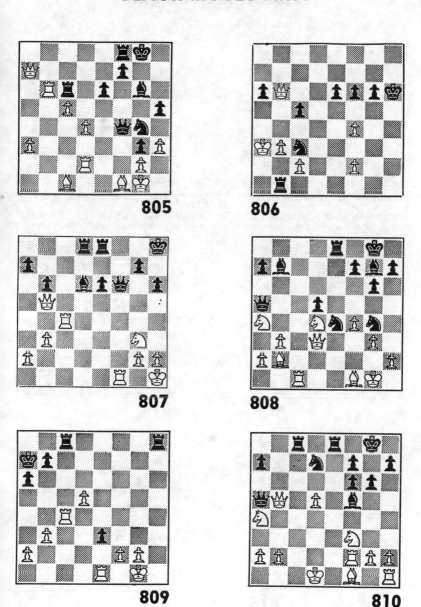

805

806

807

808

809

810

BLACK MOVES FIRST

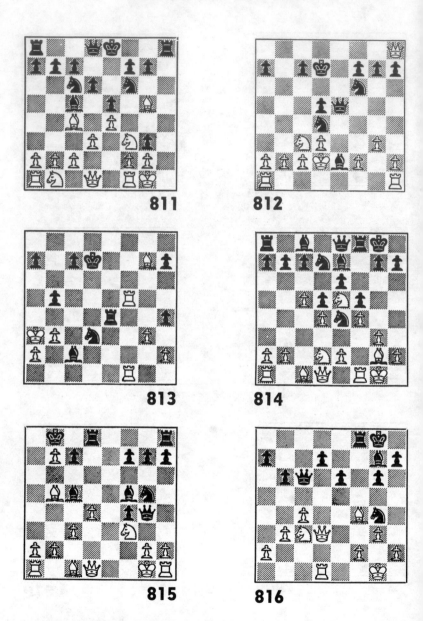

811

812

813

814

815

816

16. Defensive Combinations

This may seem a surprising subject for a book on tactical motifs. But defense is not merely passive, and in fact the best defense is never merely passive. Resourceful defense often calls for a thorough mastery of tactics. Without such mastery many a desperate position would utterly collapse.

In Diagram 824, for example, White, who is just about to lose his Queen, seems on the point of resigning. Yet he evolves a neat plan for winning Black's Queen in return. And in the last analysis this plan depends on a Knight fork.

No less ingenious is White's procedure in Diagram 827. Menaced with a mating attack, he gives up his Queen and soon demonstrates that it is Black's King, and not his own, that is fatally menaced.

In Diagram 830, too, White is threatened with mate. Yet he fights out his way out in such an ingenious manner that it is Black who gets mated.

Such examples show us the power of active, ingenious defense—really counterattack. It has been well said that counterattack is the best defense.

BLACK MOVES FIRST

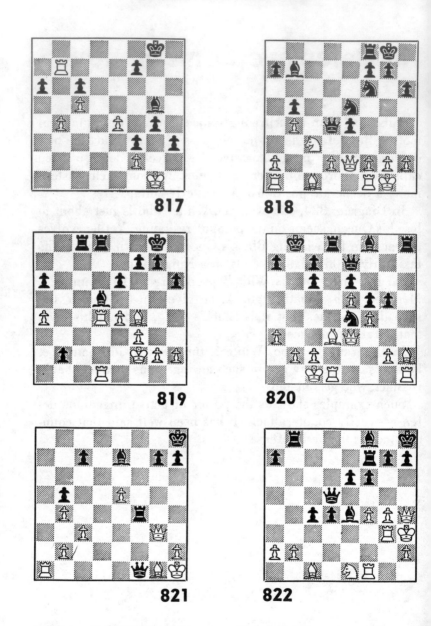

817

818

819

820

821

822

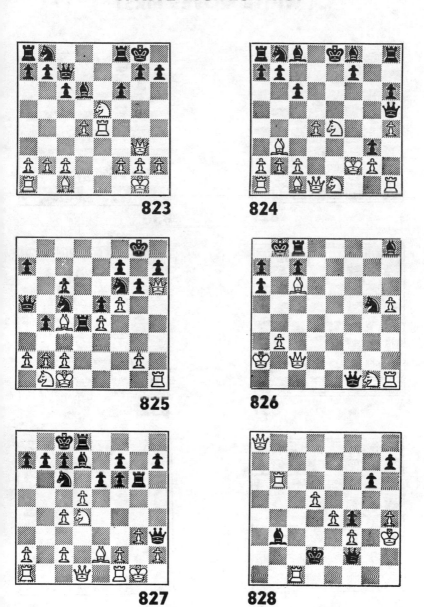

823

824

825

826

827

828

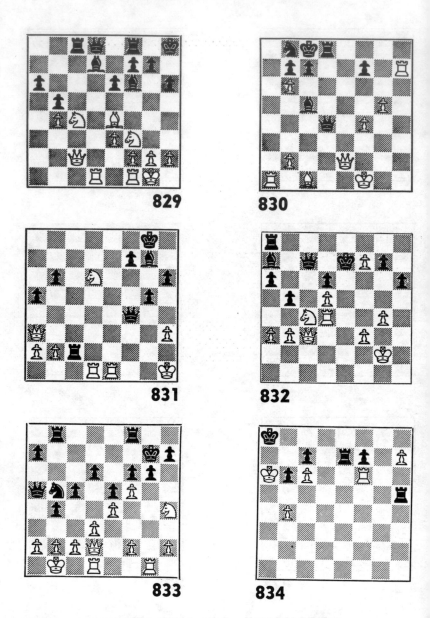

829

830

831

832

833

834

WHITE MOVES FIRST

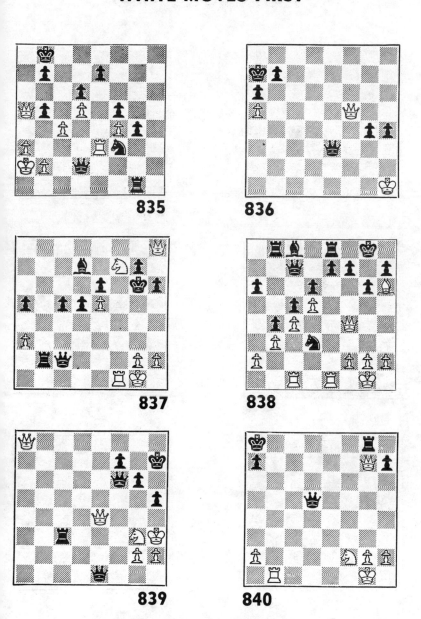

835

836

837

838

839

840

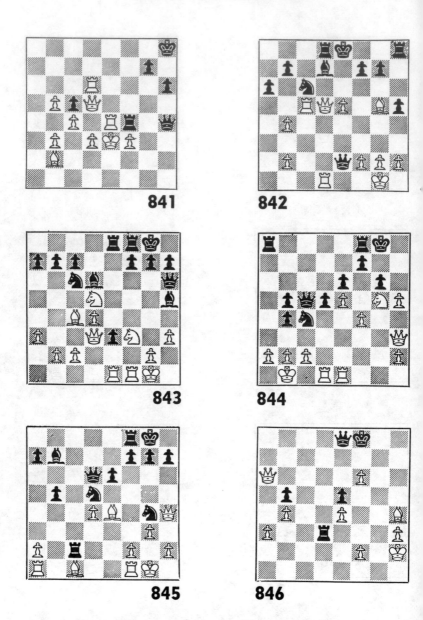

841

842

843

844

845

846

17. Trapped Man

The most common example of this theme is the trapping of a Bishop in a net of Pawns, as shown in Diagram 854. (This opening trap is so old that it is called "the Noah's Ark Trap.")

But other units can be trapped, too, and strangely enough the Queen, the mightiest of all the pieces, is particularly vulnerable to a pincer movement executed by pieces of lesser value.

That is what happens, for example, in Diagrams 847, 849, and 851. The moral is that the Queen is too valuable to be squandered on aimless expeditions without adequate support.

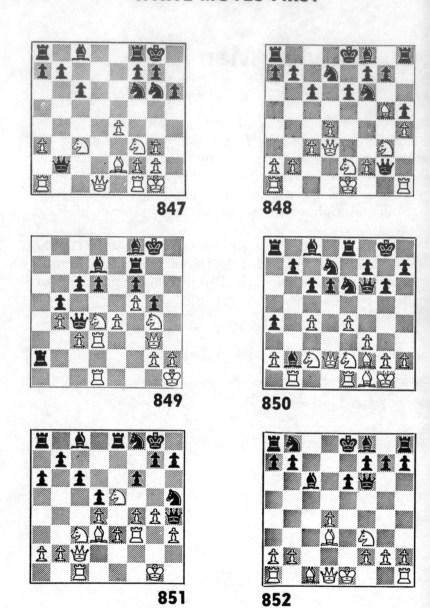

847

848

849

850

851

852

170 · TRAPPED MAN ·

BLACK MOVES FIRST

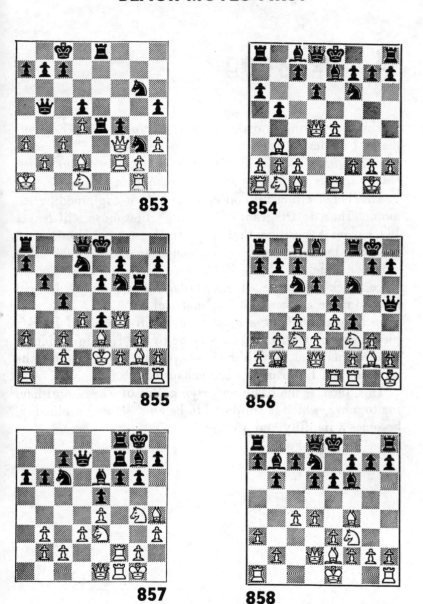

853

854

855

856

857

858

18. Zugzwang

This is a German word, not easy to translate into English; the best rendering is perhaps "compelled to move." It refers to *a position in which a player is not menaced, but which results in loss for him as soon as he makes a move.*

This is not a difficult concept, but is best explained by example. Thus, in Diagram 859, White's first move still leaves Black with a position that is perfectly secure. However, a glance at the position shows that any move of a Black *piece* will lose material. Hence Black is restricted to Pawn moves. Once Black has made all the available Pawn moves, he will have to move a piece and lose material.

In Diagram 860 we see the same picture. Some of Black's pieces are immobilized, and a move by the remaining pieces will lose material. So White simply plays 1 P—R4! and waits until Black's Pawn moves are exhausted.

This, then, is the basic underlying idea of *Zugzwang*: having to move, which is supposed to be an asset and a blessing, becomes a liability and a curse.

WHITE MOVES FIRST

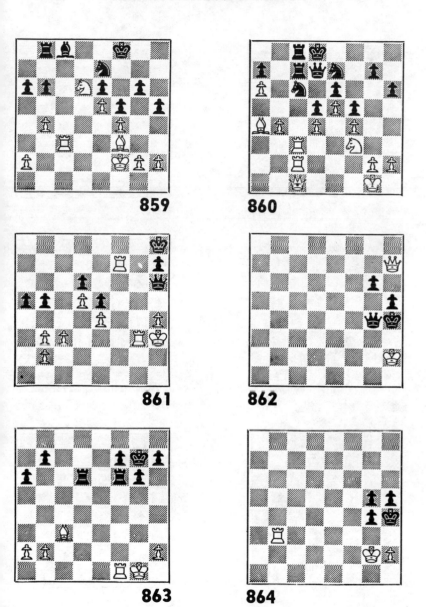

859

860

861

862

863

864

BLACK MOVES FIRST

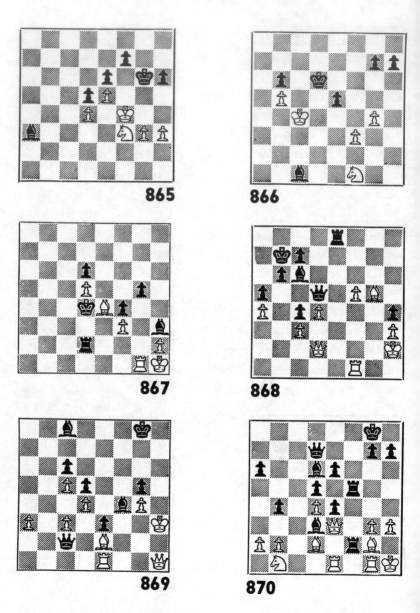

865

866

867

868

869

870

19. The Helpless King

When you are subjecting your opponent's King to a very powerful attack and he lacks adequate support by his pieces, you can make all sorts of brilliant sacrifices.

In Diagram 873, for example, Black runs into one of the most curious checkmates ever performed on the chessboard. His King is driven right down the board and mated by a castling move! Such extraordinary happenings are to be expected when a King has already been harried toward the center of the board.

In Diagram 879 the conclusion is even more picturesque. But what can Black expect with his Queen buried at Queen Rook 1, far from the scene of action? Incidentally, the absence of the defending Queen from the critical zone of attack is often the key to a brilliant combination. Diagram 885 is another case in point, and so is Diagram 889.

Even in the endgame stage, with material greatly simplified, the King may be exposed to serious tactical dangers. Thus, in Diagram 871 White drives the Black King into a mating net, while in Diagram 899 Black's King succumbs to a strikingly artistic finish.

All the examples in this section prove this point: the helpless King is a target for brilliant sacrifices and combinations.

WHITE MOVES FIRST

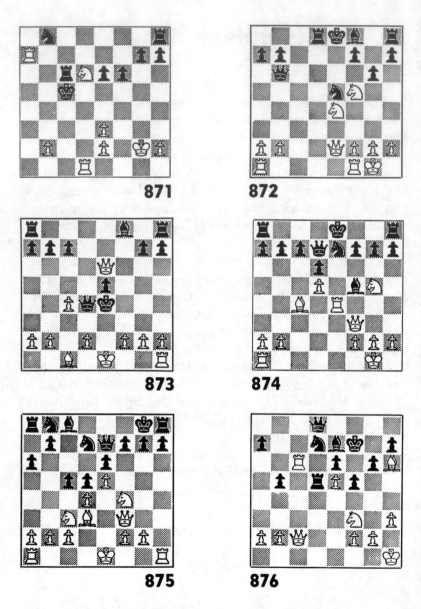

871

872

873

874

875

876

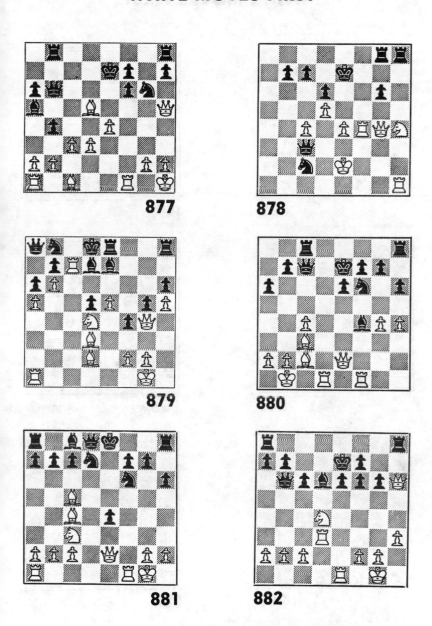

877

878

879

880

881

882

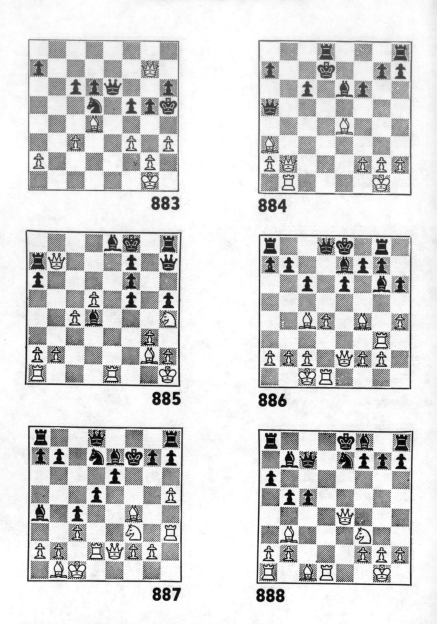

883

884

885

886

887

888

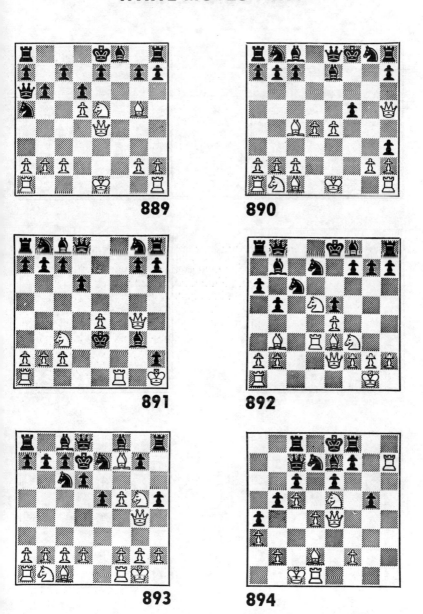

889

890

891

892

893

894

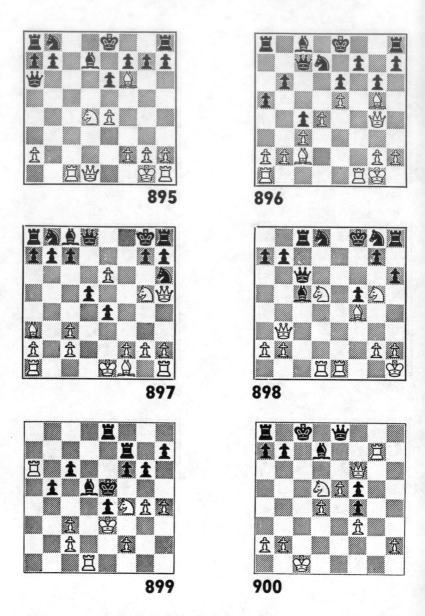

895

896

897

898

899

900

180 · The HELPLESS KING ·

BLACK MOVES FIRST

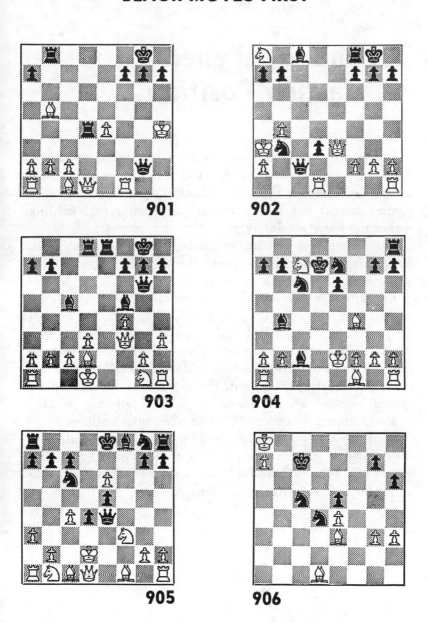

901

902

903

904

905

906

20. The Weakened Castled Position

In the previous section you've seen how the unprotected, uncastled King becomes the target of many kinds of brilliant attack. By castling, the King acquires a certain immunity against attack; but it is a mistake to assume that castling makes the King absolutely safe.

For example, a gap in the castled Pawn position (as in Diagrams 911 and 917) exposes the castled King to attack, and often brings on a devastating finish.

Likewise, the advance of one or more of the Pawns in the castled position (as in Diagrams 908, 912, and 924) creates targets for hostile attack. Brilliant sacrifices are the order of the day, and while they dazzle us, we must not forget that the positional weakness is the source of the attacker's inspiration.

As previously pointed out, the absence of the defender's Queen from the scene of action may prove costly to him. This is made clear in Diagrams 925 and 926, among others.

Note also that many attacks are brilliantly successful when they make use of open lines leading to the hostile King. Diagrams 928, 929, 932, and 941 are among the many valuable examples of this instructive theme.

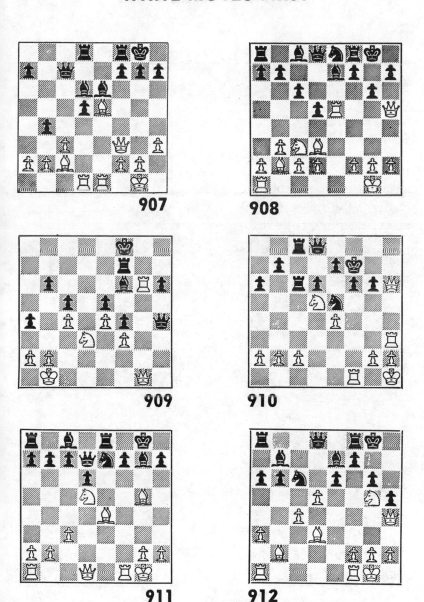

907

908

909

910

911

912

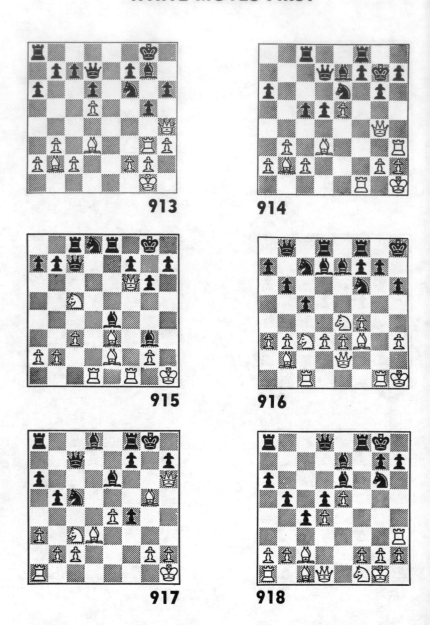

913

914

915

916

917

918

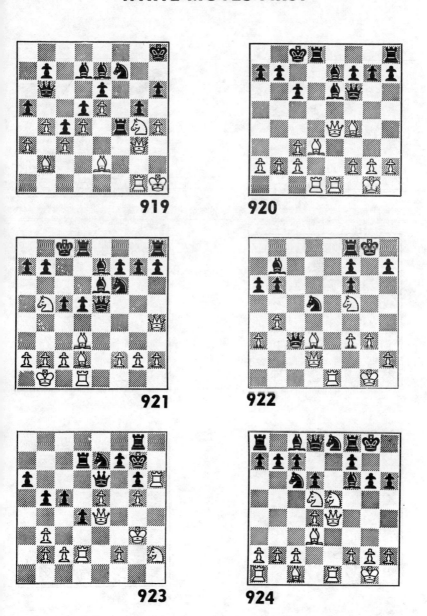

919

920

921

922

923

924

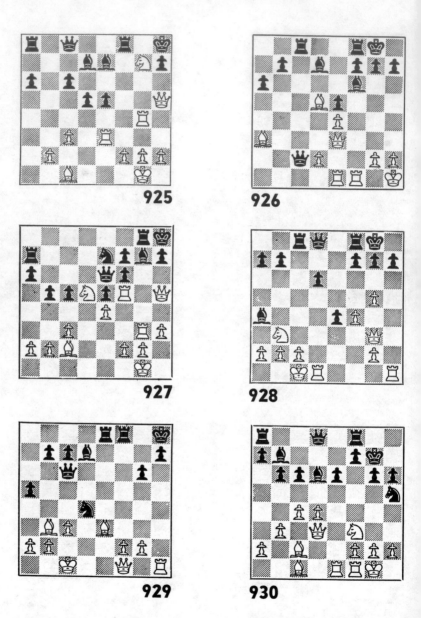

925

926

927

928

929

930

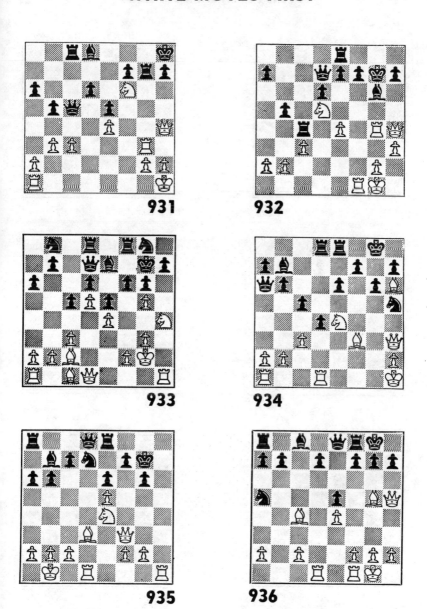

931

932

933

934

935

936

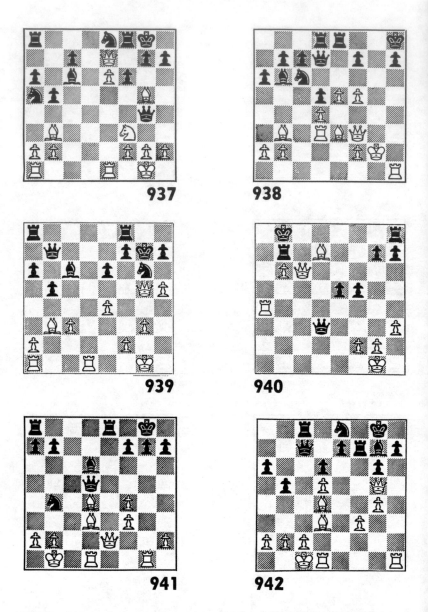

937

938

939

940

941

942

188 · The WEAKENED CASTLED POSITION ·

WHITE MOVES FIRST

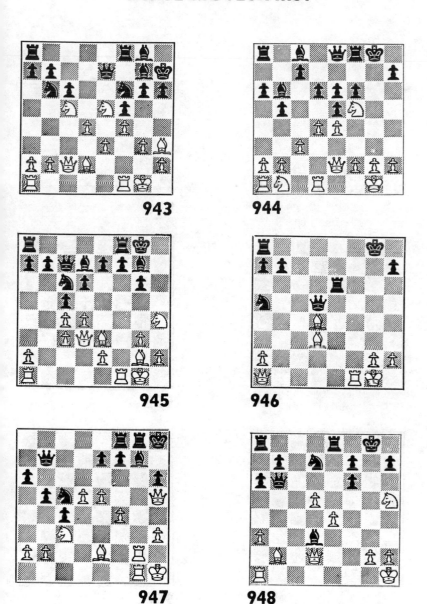

943

944

945

946

947

948

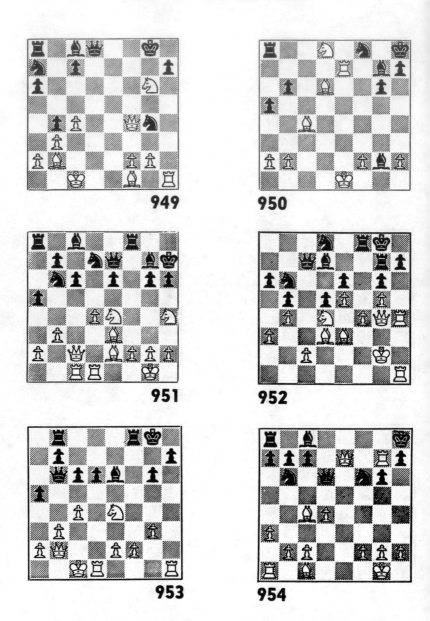

949

950

951

952

953

954

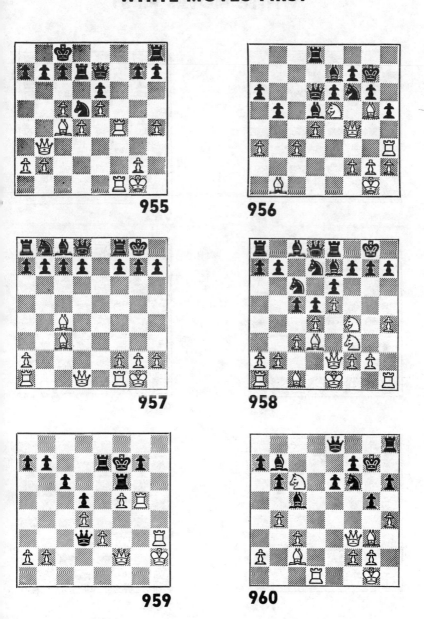

955

956

957

958

959

960

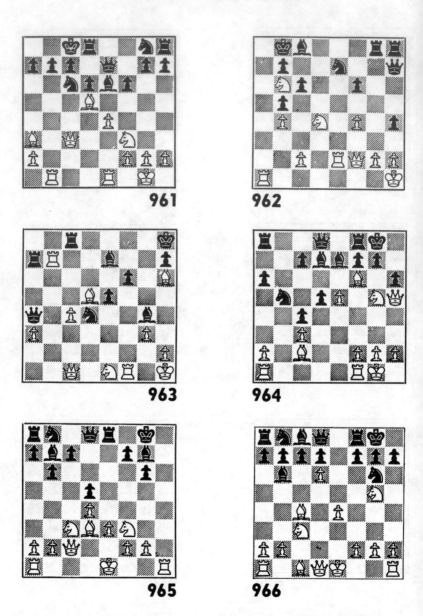

961

962

963

964

965

966

WHITE MOVES FIRST

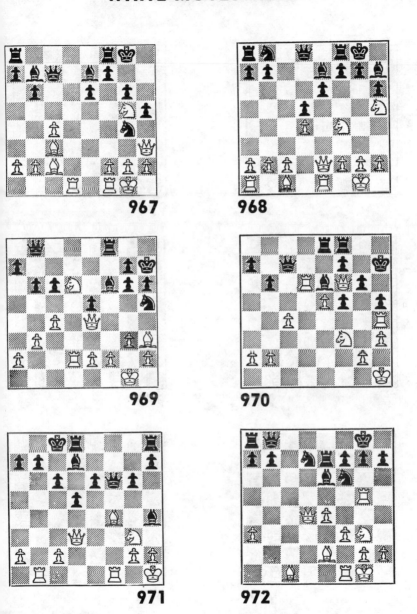

967

968

969

970

971

972

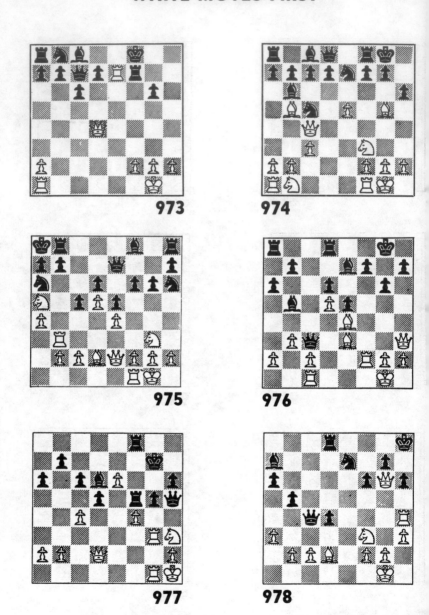

973

974

975

976

977

978

194 · The WEAKENED CASTLED POSITION ·

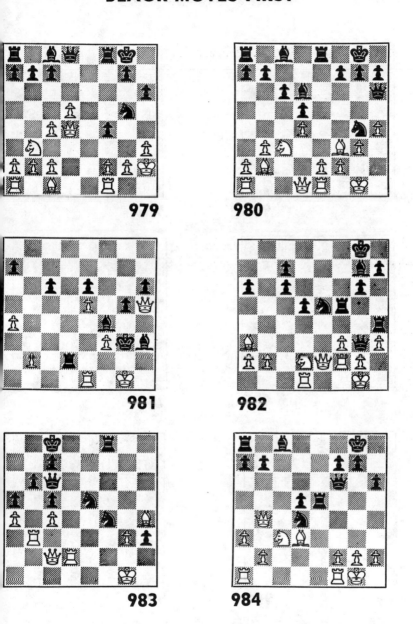

979

980

981

982

983

984

· The WEAKENED CASTLED POSITION · 195

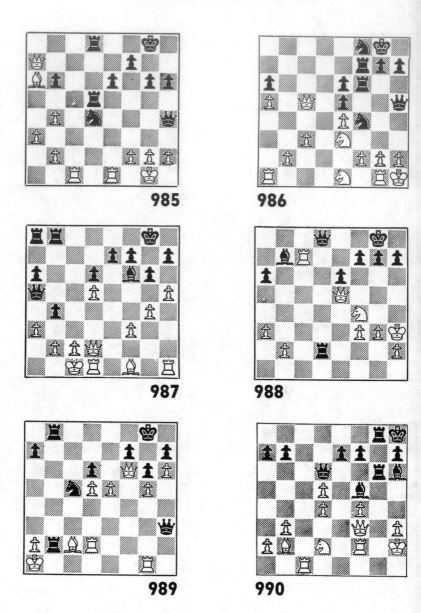

985

986

987

988

989

990

196 · The WEAKENED CASTLED POSITION ·

BLACK MOVES FIRST

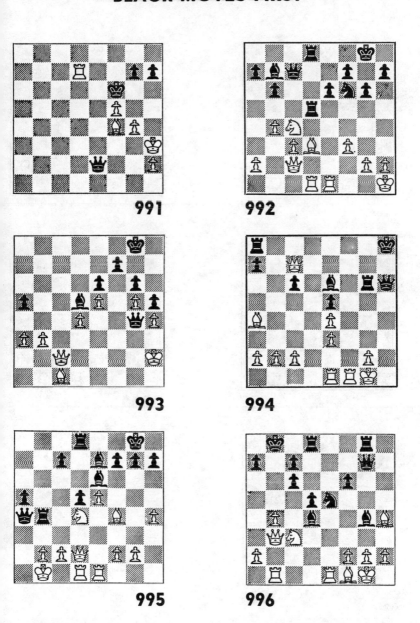

991

992

993

994

995

996

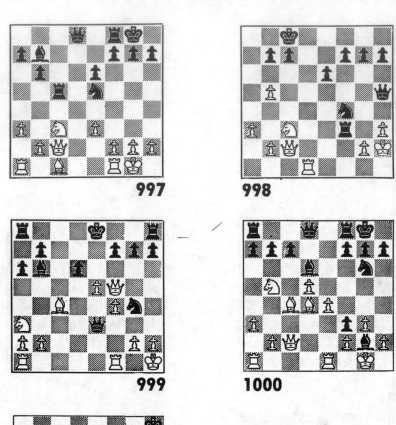

997

998

999

1000

1001

198 · The WEAKENED CASTLED POSITION ·

Solutions

1 White piles up on the pinned piece:

1	R—Q1!	QxQ
2	RxRch	K moves
3	PxQ	Resigns

2

1	R—K8!!	QxR
2	QxNch	K—N1
3	B—R6	Q—B2
4	Q—Q8ch	Q—B1
5	QxQ mate	

3

1	P—B4!	N—K2

If 1 ... NxP; 2 RxN.

2	P—B5	....

Winning the pinned piece.

4 White wins a piece:

1	BxN!	QxB
2	QxQ	PxQ
3	BxB etc.	

5

1	RxN!	PxR
2	B—R8!	Resigns

Black is helpless against the coming Q—N7 mate.

6

1	Q—R4ch!	K—N1
2	Q—N3ch!	K—R1
3	B—B3	....

White wins the Queen.

7

1	Q—N8ch!!	K—K2

If 1 ... KxQ; 2 N—N6! followed by R—R8 mate!

2	QxBPch	K—Q1
3	N—N6	QxNP
4	R—Q1ch	B—Q2
5	QxRch!	Resigns

For if 5 ... KxQ; 6 R—R8 mate.

8 White wins a Rook:

1	B—K4!	QxQ
2	BxQ etc.	

9

1	NxB	RxN
2	BxN!	RxB
3	P—N6	....

White wins a piece.

10

1	N—Q6!	R—K2
2	N/R4xP	BxN
3	NxB	R—K3
4	B—N3 and wins	

11 White keeps the extra piece by a counter-pin:

1	Q—R8!	Resigns

12

1	N—K7ch!	QxN
2	RxQ etc.	

If 2 ... RxQ; 3 R—K8 mate.

13

1	NxBP	Q—Q2
2	N—K7ch!	QxN
3	QxR etc.	

White has won the Exchange.

14

1	Q—N7!	KR—B1

If 1 ... Q—Q3; 2 NxN, PxN; 3 RxP etc.

2	NxP!	Q—Q3

If 2 ... PxN; 3 RxR etc.

3	RxP!!	Resigns

If 3 ... RxR; 4 QxQRch winning more material.

15

1	N—B7ch!	R/B2xN

Not 1 ... BxN?; 2 QxN mate.

2	PxR and wins	

Black has no defense to the coming RxB, as his King Rook Pawn is pinned.

16

1	BxN!	PxR
2	R—KN1 and wins	

17 White "piles up" on the pinned Knight and wins it:

1	B—B4 etc.	

18

1	N—Q7!!	NxN
2	QxBch	QxQ
3	BxQch	R—B2
4	BxRch and wins	

19

1	R—KN4!	Resigns

If 1 ... QxR; 2 QxPch and 3 QxP mate.

20

1	BxN!	Resigns

If 1 ... PxB; 2 RxQ; or 1 ... BxB; 2 QxBPch winning.

21

1	RxPch!!	KxR
2	R—N1 and wins	

22

1	BxP!	QxB
2	R—B7	R—K2
3	RxR	QxR
4	R—B7	Resigns

23　　1 N—B7ch　　　K—N1
　　　2 N—Q6 dis ch Q—K3
　　　3 R—K1!! and wins
　　If 3 . . . QxQ; 4 RxR mate.

24　　1 Q—KN1!　　　R—K1
　　White threatened mate.
　　　2 B—R5!　　　　R—Q1
　　　3 Q—R2　　　Resigns
　　The Knight is lost.

25　　1 P—N4ch!　　　KxP
　　　2 B—K6 and wins

26　　1 RxB!　　　　　RxR
　　　2 R—KB1　　　QR—KB1
　　　3 Q—N5　　　　K—N2
　　　4 RxR　　　　　RxR
　　　5 BxRch　　　　QxB
　　　6 N—R5ch　　　....
　　White wins the Queen.

27　　1 PxPch　　　　BxP
　　　2 RxB!　　　　　RxR
　　　3 R—KB1　　　　R—B1
　　　4 R—B3!　　　R/B1—B3
　　　5 K—B2! and wins
　　White wins the pinned piece by 6
　　K—N3 and 7 K—N4.

28　　1 N—B7!　　　　QxN
　　　2 QxR　　　　　....
　　White has won the Exchange.

29　　1 B—N5!　　　　PxB
　　　2 PxP　　　　　....
　　Black must save his Queen, allow-
　　ing White's 3 RxR.

30　　1 R—QN3!　　　PxR
　　If Black's Queen retreats, White
　　has a winning attack.
　　　2 QxQ and wins
　　Black's Bishop Pawn is pinned!

31　　1 NxN!!　　　　BxQ
　　　2 B—N5ch　　　P—QB3
　　　3 PxP and wins
　　The double threat of 4 PxP dis ch
　　and 4 P—B7 dis ch is decisive.

32　　1 NxP!　　　　　NxN
　　　2 Q—N4! and wins
　　The double threat of 3 QxNch
　　and 3 QxBch is too strong.

33　　1 BxN!　　　　　BxB
　　Or 1 . . . PxB; 2 N—K5 with a
　　winning pin on the open file.
　　　2 RxQch and wins

34　　1 NxKP!　　　Resigns
　　White wins the Queen, as 1 . . .
　　PxN allows 2 Q—Q8 mate.

35　　1 NxKPch!　　　PxN
　　　2 RxPch!　　　Resigns
　　If 2 . . . PxR; 3 Q—N8 mate. If
　　2 . . . K—K1; 3 RxP wins easily.

36　　1 N—K7ch!　　Resigns
　　If 1 . . . QxN; 2 QxBch, Q—B1;
　　3 B—R7ch wins the Queen.

37　　1 BxPch!　　　　RxB
　　　2 RxN/K4!　　　QxR
　　　3 QxRch　　　　K—R1
　　　4 N/B3—K4!　　....
　　If now 4 . . . B—Q5; 5 BxB, QxB;
　　6 QxRch! forces mate. And if 4 . . .
　　Q—K2; 5 RxN! etc.
　　　4 ....　　　　　QxB
　　　5 NxN　　　　　Q—K7
　　　6 Q—N8ch!　　　RxQ
　　　7 N—B7 mate

38　　1 NxNP!!　　　　BxN
　　　2 RxB!　　　　　RxR
　　　3 BxP　　　　　NxBP
　　　4 RxR!　　　　　QxR
　　If 4 . . . NxQ; 5 RxQ dis ch,
　　K—R1; 6 RxR and wins.
　　　5 BxQch　　　　KxB
　　　6 Q—N4ch　　　Resigns

39　　1 P—K5!　　　　BxP
　　　2 NxB　　　　　QxN
　　　3 R—K1　　　　N—K5
　　　4 P—KB3 and wins

40　　1 NxN　　　　　BxN
　　　2 N—R5ch!　　　PxN
　　　3 Q—N5ch!　　　K—R1
　　　4 BxBch　　　　....
　　White wins the Queen.

41　　1 B—N1!　　　　....
　　Threatens 2 BxN and 3 QxP mate.
　　　1 ....　　　　　P—N3
　　　2 BxN!　　　　　BxB
　　　3 N—K4!　　　Resigns
　　For after 3 . . . B—K2; 4 P—
　　QN4 wins the pinned Knight.

42　　Black threatens to break out of
　　the pin with . . . N—B6ch. But
　　White is alert:
　　　1 K—B1!　　　　K—N2
　　　2 R—B2　　　　K—B3
　　　3 R/B2—K2　　P—KR4
　　　4 RxN　　　　　Resigns

200 · SOLUTIONS ·

43
   1 P—K5!   PxP
   2 NxB   KxN
   3 B—N5   B—B4
   4 NxBch   PxN
   5 QxP   Q—Q3
   6 R—Q1!   Q—K3
   7 BxNch   Resigns
If 1 . . . QxB; 8 R—Q7ch wins.

44
   1 NxP!   B—QB2
If 1 . . . NxN??; 2 Q—K8 mate;
and on 1 . . . PxN; 2 QxB wins.
   2 N—Q5!   Resigns
If 2 . . . BxN; 3 N—Q7ch wins
the Queen. If 2 . . . QxB; 3 NxB
attacks the Queen and threatens 4
Q—K8 mate.

45 White has a slow win with 1
NxQ, RxRch; 2 KxR, BxQ; 3 NxP
etc. Much faster is:
   1 B—QR3!   BxN
Or 1 . . . QxB; 2 QxP mate.
   2 BxQch and wins

46
   1 P—B6!   RxP!
If now 2 RxR? Black is stalemated!
   2 P—B7!   R—QB3
   3 R—R6!   Resigns
If 3 . . . RxR; 4 P—B8/Q mate.

47
   1 P—Q5!!   PxP
   2 NxN   Q—Q2
If 2 . . . BxN; 3 QxBch wins.
   3 N—R5!   Resigns
The double threat of 4 NxB and
4 BxP decides.

48
   1 R—K6!   Resigns
If 1 . . . PxR; 2 QxPch, K—R1;
3 BxNch and 4 Q—R7 mate.

49
   1 RxN!   RxR
   2 R—Q1   Q—K3
   3 BxRch   NxB
   4 Q—N8ch!   NxQ
   5 R—Q8 mate

50
   1 P—KN4!   Resigns
If Black moves the attacked
Knight, he loses the other Knight.
And if 1 . . . PxP; 2 NxP/N4 win-
ning the pinned Knight.

51
   1 B—B5!   K—B1
   2 Q—B6!   Resigns
White wins the miserable Bishop.

52
   1 Q—B4!   N—K3
   2 Q—QR4ch! Q—B3
   3 B—QN5   . . . .
White wins the Queen.

53
   1 B—N5!!   RxB
   2 QR—Q1   Q—B1
   3 Q—K3! and wins
White's mating threat forces 3 . . .
Castles, and after 4 QxR White is
the Exchange ahead.

54
   1 Q—K3!   Q—N1
If 1 . . . Q—Q3; 2 N—B6ch wins
Black's Queen. If 1 . . . BxN; 2 RxB,
N—Q2; 3 Q—Q4 wins the pinned
Knight.
   2 R—K1   BxN
   3 BxBch   N—B2
   4 R—KB1   Resigns
White wins the pinned Knight.

55
   1 N—B5!!   PxN
   2 B—B4!   Q—Q3
If 2 . . . QxB; 3 Q—B8ch, K—K2;
4 QxR wins. If 2 . . . Q—Q1; 3
QxR etc. wins.
   3 BxB   R—N3
   4 QxNch!   Resigns
White comes out a piece up.

56
   1 P—B6!   B—N5
If 1 . . . PxP; 2 Q—N6ch followed by 3 Q—R7 mate.
   2 Q—N6!   Resigns
White forces 3 QxNP mate or 3
Q—R7 mate.

57
   1 BxN!   BxB
Or 1 . . . PxB; 2 Q—N4ch, K—
R1; 3 NxPch winning the Exchange.
   2 QxPch!!   KxQ
   3 R—R5ch   K—N1
   4 N—N6!   Resigns
For 5 R—R8 mate follows.

58
   1 P—B5!   P—K5
The Bishop is helpless.
   2 PxB!   PxN
   3 P—Q7!   Resigns
White attacks Knight and Rook.

59
   1 NxN!!   Q—R4ch
Or 1 . . . BxQ; 2 B—N5ch, Q—
Q2; 3 BxQch, K—Q1; 4 NxPch,
KxB; 5 KxB and White has won too
much material.
   2 B—Q2   BxQ
   3 BxQ   PxN
   4 B—N5 mate!

60   1 Q—B6 mate

61   1 B—Q4!   P—K4
        2 BxP!   QxB
        3 Q—R6 mate

62   1 RxB!   QxR
        2 Q—B3   K—N2
If 2 . . . B—B4; 3 NxB, PxN; 4
Q—N3!, K—N2; 5 BxN dbl ch,
KxB; 6 Q—R4ch!, K—K3; 7 R—
K1ch winning.
        3 N/B3—K4!!   PxN
        4 NxP   Q—K3
Or 4 . . . QxN; 5 QxNch, K—N1;
6 B—R6 followed by mate.
        5 BxNch   K—N1
        6 Q—B4   Resigns
For 7 Q—R6 wins.

63   1 R—K1!!   RxP
If 1 . . . BxB; 2 QxQ wins.
        2 BxBch   QxB
        3 Q—R7ch   B—N2
        4 QxPch   Resigns
White wins on material.

64   1 B—B4   Resigns

65   1 BxNch   PxB
        2 NxP!!   Resigns
If 2 . . . RxQch; 3 RxR and
Black's Queen is trapped because of
the mate threat (3 . . . Q—K3??;
4 R—Q8 mate). After 3 . . . Q—Q2;
4 RxQ, KxR; 5 NxP White wins
easily.

66   1 QxPch!!   KxQ
        2 R—KR5 mate

67   1 QxN!!   PxQ
Or 1 . . . BxR; 2 RxB! with material plus.
        2 BxPch   K—R1
        3 N—N6ch   K—R2
        4 NxR dbl ch K—R1
        5 N—N6ch   K—R2
        6 N—K5 dis ch! K—R1
        7 N—B7 mate

68   1 RxR   PxR
        2 P—K6!   QxQ
        3 NxQ   ....
White wins the Bishop.

69   1 R—N3!   PxR
        2 BxQ and wins

70   1 RxN!!   PxR
        2 N—K6ch!!   PxN
        3 R—B7ch   Resigns
White continues 4 QxQ.

71   1 NxP!   QNxN
        2 RxN!   NxN
        3 RxN!   QxR
        4 N—N5!!   Q—N3
If 4 . . . QxQ; 5 N—B7 mate!
        5 QxPch!!   QxQ
        6 N—B7 mate

72   1 N—N6!   Resigns
White wins the Queen!

73   1 ....   QxPch!
        2 QxQ   RxR
    Resigns

74   1 ....   P—Q5!!
        2 QxP   Q—R8ch
This wins White's Knight (after
3 Q—Q1 etc.) as 3 N—Q1?? allows
3 . . . QxQ.

75   1 ....   RxPch!!
        2 BxR   QxBch etc.
Black's counter-pin wins for him!

76   1 ....   B—R3!!
        2 P—KN5   BxP!
        3 P—B4   BxP!
        4 B—K3   BxB
        5 QxB   QxBP mate

77   1 ....   N—N6ch!
        2 PxN   Q—R6ch
        3 K—N1   BxBch
        Resigns
If 4 QxB or 4 R—B2 Black has
4 . . . QxP/N7 mate.

78   1 ....   R/B1—B6!
        2 Q—K2   B—N4!
If now 3 BxB, RxB wins a piece
for Black.
        3 R/B1—Q1   Q—B2!
        4 B—Q4   RxB!
        5 RxR   Q—B5!
        Resigns
Black comes out a piece to the
good.

79   1 ....   Q—N3!
If now 2 N/B3—K2, Black wins a
piece by 2 . . . P—K4.
        2 B—K3   P—K4
        3 N—R4   Q—R2!
Black must win a piece.

80   1 ....   N—K5!!
If now 2 BxQ, BxP mate!
2 B—K3   BxB
3 PxB   Q—R5ch
4 P—KN3   NxNP
Black has a winning game.

81   1 ....   Q—B4!!
2 N—B3   KR—K1!
3 R—K1   RxB!
4 NxR   R—K1
5 P—KN4   RxN!!
Resigns
If 6 PxQ, RxR mate.

82   1 ....   N—B6
White has nothing better than 2
NxN, RxR leaving him with a lost
game.

83   1 ....   RxPch!
2 K—Q1   RxBch!
Resigns
For after 3 KxR Black exploits
the new pin decisively with 3 . . .
N—K5ch etc.

84   1 ....   N/B5xQP!
2 PxN   NxQP
3 R—B4   B—N4!
By winning the Rook, Black un-
dermines White's advanced Bishop.
4 Q—K4   BxR
5 RxB   RxR
and wins

85   1 ....   R/K1xN!
2 PxR   Q—R5
3 BxP   RxB
4 N—K2   BxN
5 RxR   N—N6ch!
6 K—N1   B—B4ch
7 R—B2   Q—B5
Resigns

86   1 ....   NxNP!
If 2 BxN, Q—R5ch etc.
2 Q—K2   Q—R5ch
Resigns
For if 3 B—B2, NxB; 4 QxN,
QxQch; 5 KxQ, B—N5 and the pin
wins a piece. Or 3 K—Q1, NxBch;
4 QxN, RxB!; 5 QxR, B—N5 with
an even more disastrous pin.

87   1 ....   P—Q5!
If now 2 QxP, QxBP mate!
2 PxP   B—N5!
This wins the Queen, for if 3 QxB,
QxBP mate!

88   1 ....   RxN!
Resigns
If 2 QPxR, Q—Q8 mate.

89   1 ....   N—B6ch!
2 QxN   ....
If 2 K—N2, NxRch wins the Exchange, while if 2 K—R1, NxR!; 3
QxQ?, R—B8 mate!
2 ....   QxRch!
Black comes out the Exchange
ahead.

90   1 ....   R—K8!
2 QxR   NxBch
And Black wins the Queen.

91   1 ....   R—R3ch!
2 K—N1   R—R8ch!!
3 KxR   Q—R6ch
4 K—N1   QxP/N7 mate

92   1 ....   PxB!
2 RxQ   R—D0ch!
3 K—N2   R/B4—B7 mate

93   1 ....   BxP!
2 RxR   ....
Even better for Black is 2 QxB,
RxR etc.
2 ....   B—B3 dis ch!
and wins

94   1 ....   BxBch
2 NxB   Q—N3!
3 QxP   NxP!
This wins, for after 4 Q—Q7, N—
Q3! or 4 Q—K5, R—K3! the White
Knight is lost.

95   1 ....   BxPch!
If now 2 KxB?, QxQ wins.
2 K—B1   BxR and wins

96   1 ....   RxP!
If now 2 R—R3, R/Q5—Q8 wins
the Knight "to begin with."
2 RxR   BxR
White is helpless against 3 . . .
R—B7 winning his Rook.

97   1 ....   K—R2!
2 B—K1   K—R3!
3 B—B3   K—R4!
4 B—K1   K—N5!
5 B—B3   PxPch
6 RxPch   K—R6!
7 any   BxR mate

· **SOLUTIONS** · **203**

98
1	QxRch!
2 KxQ	PxQ
Resigns	

99
1	B—N4!
2 P—B4	BxP!
3 QxB	QxP mate

100
1	RxN!
2 QxR	NxKP

Threatens ... N—N6 mate or ... N—B7 mate, aside from attacking White's Queen. So:

3 Q—N2	N—B7 mate!

101
1	RxB!
2 RxR	Q—QN2!
3 Q—KN2	Q—N8ch!

But not 3 . . . N—B5?; 4 R—Q8ch!

4 Q—N1	Q—K5ch!
5 Q—N2	QxQch
6 KxQ	N—B5ch

Black wins the Rook and remains a piece ahead.

102
1	R—N5!!
Resigns	

For if 2 BxR, QxR/B8 mate!

103
1	B—N5!
2 QxB	NxPch

Winning White's Queen.

104
1	RxP!!
2 QxR	Q—R4ch!
3 R—R3	Q—K4ch
4 K—R1	Q—K8ch
5 K—R2	Q—KN8 mate

105
1	P—R5!
2 N—B1	P—R6!

Black wins the Bishop.

106
1	NxP!
2 PxN	RxPch!!
3 QxR	RxN mate

107 Black gets nowhere with ... PxN. Instead, by playing 1 . . . Q—K2 he pins and wins the Knight. Another way is 1 . . . R—K3 and if 2 Q—KB2, Q—K2; 3 N—Q2, R—K7 etc.

108
1	QxR!
2 NxQ	BxQ
Resigns	

109
1 QxN!	QxQ
2 NxBch	K—R1
3 NxQ and wins	

110
1 N—Q6ch	K—B1

Black loses his Queen after 1 . . . BxN?

2 NxB and wins	

111
1 BxB	KxB
2 BxN	KxB
3 N—Q6ch and wins	

After 4 NxR White is a Rook ahead.

112
1 N—Q6ch	BxN
2 NxBch	K moves
3 NxBP and wins	

White will be the Exchange and a Pawn ahead.

113 White wins the Queen:
1 RxRch	RxR
2 RxRch	QxR
3 NxPch	Resigns

114
1 N—B7ch!	K—K2

If 1 . . . RxN; 2 RxRch with the Exchange ahead.

2 RxR	RxR
3 RxR	KxR
4 N—K6ch and wins	

White's next is 5 NxB.

115
1 N—Q5!	QxBP

If 1 . . . PxN; 2 Q—B7ch and 3 QxNP mate. If 1 . . . Q—R3; 2 Q—N4, P—QN3; 3 NxP and wins (or 2 . . . P—N4; 3 Q—R5 and wins).

2 RxNPch!	KxR
3 Q—N4ch	K—B1

Or 3 . . . K—R1; 4 N—B7 mate.

4 N—K7ch	....

The fork wins the Queen.

116
1 N—Q6	B—Q2

White threatened N—B5ch as well as NxB.

2 R—K7ch	K—B3
3 RxB	K—K3
4 R—Q8	K—K2
5 N—B5ch and wins	

117
1 Q—R8ch!	K—R2
2 N—B3 and wins	

White wins the Exchange.

118 1 QxQ   BxQ
      2 RxR   RxR
      3 N—B7ch and wins

119 1 NxQP!   BxN
White was threatening NxQ in addition to Q—R8 mate.
      2 N—Q7ch and wins
White wins the Queen. (1 N—Q7ch also wins, but less simply.)

120 1 RxN!   QxR
      2 QxRch!   KxQ
      3 N—N6ch and wins
White will be a piece ahead.

121 After 1 PxR/Q, RxQch Black can still fight on. So:
      1 PxR/N!   RxQch
      2 NxRch   K moves
      3 NxB and wins

122 1 N—R7!   ....
Black must move his Queen, allowing 2 NxR. If instead 1 ... KxN; 2 QxPch and 3 Q—R7 mate.

123 1 N—N5ch   K—N1
      2 Q—R7ch   K—B1
      3 N—Q6ch   ....
White wins the Queen.

124 1 N—N6ch!   PxN
      2 B—K6
White wins the Queen.

125 1 R—R5ch!   K—B3
If 1 ... BxR; 2 N—K6ch wins the Queen.
      2 RxPch   ....
White wins the Knight.

126 1 N—Q5ch   Resigns
White wins the Rook.

127 1 NxKP!   Resigns
If 1 ... BxN; 2 R—N8 mate. If 1 ... PxN; 2 RxQ wins. If the Knight is not captured, White wins a Rook.

128 1 N—Q8ch!   RxN
      2 QxKPch   Resigns
Black is lost after 3 QxRch.

129 1 QxB!   RxQ
      2 N—Q7ch   K moves
      3 NxQ   ....
White has won a piece.

130 1 NxBP!   BxN
      2 N—K7ch K moves
      3 NxB and wins
White will be the Exchange and a Pawn ahead.

131 1 P—N4!   B—N3
      2 P—N5   N—R4
      3 N—K7ch   ....
White wins the Queen.

132 The immediate QxR will not do because of ... QxRch. Therefore:
      1 N—B7ch!   K—N1
If 1 ... RxN; 2 Q—B8ch leads to mate.
      2 N—R6ch   K—R1
      3 QxPch!!   KxQ
      4 NxRch and wins

133 1 NxPch!   PxN
      2 RxPch   Resigns

134 1 RxPch!   QxR
      2 N—K7ch   Resigns
White wins the Queen.

135 1 N—B6ch!   BxN
      2 QxPch   any
      3 Q—R7 mate

136 1 N—B6ch!   PxN
      2 Q—KN3ch Resigns
If 2 ... B—N2; 3 BxP etc.

137 1 N—Q6ch!   BxN
      2 RxNch   B—K2
      3 RxBch   KxR
      4 N—B6ch   Resigns
After 5 NxR White will be a piece ahead.

138 1 RxN!   QxR
      2 R—Q8!   QxR
On 2 ... Q—K2 or the like, White has 3 R—KR8 mate.
      3 NxPch   K moves
      4 NxQ and wins

139 1 P—N5ch!   Resigns
If Black takes either Knight, 2 N—Q7ch wins the Rook. If 1 ... K—B2; 2 N—K6ch with the same result.

140 1 N—B6ch   BxN
      2 PxB   Resigns
The coming check on the King file leaves Black helpless.

141 1 Q—B6! QxQ
2 NxQ ....
White threatens RxN and also
NxR and N—Q7ch.
2 .... N—B6
3 R—B4 N—Q7ch
4 K—R2 NxB
5 KxN! R—R1
6 N—Q7ch and wins
With the Exchange ahead, White
will have an easy win.

142 1 RxPch!! K—N1
If 1 . . . KxR; 2 N—N5ch! QxN;
3 Q—K6ch, K—B1; 4 QxN mate or
2 . . . K—N1; 3 Q—K6ch, K—R1;
4 N—B7ch winning the Queen.
2 N—N5! N—B3
If 2 . . . QxN; 3 RxNch, KxR;
4 Q—K6 mate.
3 RxBch Resigns
If 3 . . . KxR; 4 N—K6ch wins
the Queen.

143 1 QxR! BPxQ
2 N—B7ch and wins
After 3 NxR White will be the
Exchange ahead.

144 1 QxN! RxQ
2 N—B6ch K—K2
3 NxRch! K—K1
4 N—B6ch K—K2
5 NxQ and wins
White is the Exchange ahead.

145 1 RxP! BxR
2 Q—B3!! ....
White threatens 3 QxBch and 4
Q—K7 mate. If now 2 . . . Q—K3;
3 NxPch or if 2 . . . Q—Q2; 3
N—B6ch winning the Queen. Also
if 2 . . . B—N1; 3 Q—B8ch, K—Q2;
4 Q—N7ch, K—B3; 5 N—K7ch
with the same result.
2 .... BxN
3 BPxB! Resigns
White's mate threat decides.

146 1 QxRch! RxQ
2 N—K6ch and wins
After 3 NxQ White is a piece
ahead.

147 1 R—K8!! Q—N4
If 1 . . . QxR; 2 N—R5ch, K—
R2; 3 N—B6ch wins.
2 Q—K3 ....

Threatens 3 R—K7ch, K—B3; 4
Q—K5 mate.
2 .... P—KR4
3 Q—K5ch Resigns
If 3 . . . Q—B3; 4 R—K7ch wins
the Queen.

148 1 N—N6!! PxN
2 PxP R—B3
If 2 . . . N—B3; 3 Q—R2 forces
mate.
3 R—R8ch! Resigns
If 3 . . . KxR; 4 Q—R2ch, K—
N1; 5 Q—R7ch, K—B1; 6 Q—R8
mate.

149 1 QxB!! PxQ
2 NxNch K—R1
3 RxRch RxR
4 B—N7ch! KxB
5 NxRch K moves
6 NxQ and wins
White is a piece ahead.

150 1 RxB! PxR
2 BxP! QxB
3 NxBPch! Resigns
White wins the Queen.

151 1 .... N/K7—Q5ch!
2 PxN NxPch
3 K moves NxB etc.

152 1 .... N—R6ch
2 K—N2 N—N4
Resigns
Black wins a piece.

153 1 .... N—B5ch!
2 PxN R—K1ch
Resigns
If 3 K—Q2, Q—Q6 mate. Or 3
N—K4, RxNch winning the Queen.

154 1 .... QxR!
2 NxQ N—K7ch
Followed by 3 . . . NxQ and
Black has won the Exchange.

155 1 .... N/N4—B6ch!
2 PxN B—R5!
3 Q—N2 BxR
Black has won the Exchange.

156 1 .... QxR!
2 NxQ N—K7ch
Resigns
Black comes out a Rook ahead.

157   1 ....   R—Q7!
If now 2 QxR, N—B6ch wins the Queen.
        2 Q—B1   N—B6ch
If now 3 K—R1, RxP mate.
        3 K—B1   Q—N4ch
Or 3 . . . Q—R3ch with the same effect. Black mates next move.

158   1 ....   P—Q7ch!
        2 KxP   NxNch
        3 K moves   NxB
Black wins easily.

159   1 ....   NxR!
        2 NxQ   N—K7ch
        3 K—R1   NxQ
Black is a Rook ahead.

160   1 ....   P—QN4!
If now 2 B—N3, P—R5 wins the Bishop.
        2 BxNP   N—Q5ch
        3 NxN   NxNch
Followed by . . . NxB and wins.

161   1 ....   RxN!
        2 BxR   N—B4ch
        3 K moves   NxB and wins

162   1 ....   R—B8ch!
        2 RxR   RxRch
        3 KxR   N—N6ch
        4 K moves   NxQ and wins

163   1 ....   QxB!
        2 QxQ   N—B6ch
        3 K moves   NxQ and wins

164   1 ....   N—N6!
If now 2 R—N1, N—Q5 wins a piece.
        2 PxN   QxR
Black has won the Exchange.

165   1 ....   N—B6ch
        2 K—Q1   ....
Or 2 K—B1 with the same result.
        2 ....   P—K7ch!
        3 KxP   N—Q5ch
Followed by 4 . . . NxB and wins.

166   1 ....   RxNch!
        2 PxR   N—K6ch
        3 K moves   NxB
With Bishop, Knight and Pawn for a Rook, Black has a comfortable win.

167   1 ...   BxN
        2 PxB   N—B7
Winning the Exchange, as he threatens . . . NxPch in addition to . . . NxR.

168   1 ....   N—B4
Wins the Exchange, as White cannot play 2 R—Q7.
        2 R/N7—N1   N—Q6 and wins

169   1 ....   P—Q5!
White is lost, for if the attacked Knight moves, 2 . . . N—N6ch wins his Queen.

170   1 ....   RxR
        2 RxR   BxN
        3 KxB   NxBPch
Black wins a Pawn and the Exchange. (Another way is 1 . . . RxNch; 2 RxR, BxR etc.)

171   1 ....   RxPch!
        2 KxR   NxBPch
        3 K moves   NxR
Black has won two Pawns.

172   1 ....   NxBP!!
        2 RxN   ....
If 2 KxN, N—N5ch wins the Queen. If 2 B—B3, N/B7—N5; 3 BxN, NxB and White can resign.
        2 ....   R—B8ch
        3 B—B1   RxR
        4 N/R4—B5   PxN
        5 NxP   QxRch!
        Resigns
For if 6 KxQ, N—N5ch wins.

173   1 ....   N—K5ch!
        2 PxN   R—KB1
Black wins the Queen.

174   1 ....   QxNch!
         2 KxQ   N—K5ch
        3 K moves   NxQ
Black has won a piece.

175   1 ....   B—R6!
If now 2 PxB, N—B6ch wins the Queen; or 2 P—KB4, Q—N3! winning the Queen because of the double threat 3 . . . QxP mate and 3 . . . N—B6ch.
        2 K—R1   BxPch!
        3 KxB   Q—B6ch
        4 K—N1   Q—N5ch
        5 K—R1   N—B6

6 Q—Q1   Q—R6
Resigns
White must give up his Queen to stop mate.

176   1 ....   QxNch!
     2 KxQ   NxQPch
     3 K moves   NxQ
Black has won a second Pawn.

177   1 ....   RxB!
For 2 QxR allows mate, and if 2 RxR, N—B6ch wins.
     2 P—KR3   N—B6ch!
     3 K—B2   RxRch
     Resigns

178   1 ....   QxB!
     2 PxQ   N—K7ch
     3 K moves   NxQ
Black has won a piece.

179   1 ....   N—B7ch
Black wins the Queen.

180   1 ....   QxNch!
     2 QxQ   N—K6ch
     3 K moves   NxQ
Black has won a piece.

181 White's first move threatens mate, winning the Knight at Queen Rook 7:
     1 Q—Q4!   Resigns

182 Here too White wins at once with a double threat:
     1 Q—N5!   Resigns

183   1 NxN   BxN
     2 Q—Q4!   B—R4
     3 P—QN4   KR—Q1
     4 Q—B5 and wins
White wins a piece.

184   1 BxB   RxB
     2 RxR   NxR
     3 Q—N5ch and wins
White wins a piece.

185   1 R—K8ch!   RxR
     2 PxR/Qch   KxQ
     3 R—K3ch! and wins
If Black interposes, 4 BxPch wins the Knight. If 3 ... K—Q1 or ... K—B1; 4 BxP wins the Knight because of the threatened 5 R—K8 mate.

186   1 Q—Q4! and wins
Black must stop the mate, thereby losing his Knight.

187   1 Q—B3ch   K moves
     2 Q—K1! and wins
White wins the Rook or Bishop.

188 White's mate threat wins the Bishop:
     1 Q—K4 and wins

189   1 Q—Q8! and wins
White threatens QxB as well as R—B8ch.

190   1 R—B7!!   QxR/B2
     2 RxN!   Resigns
If 2 ... QxR; 3 QxNP mate or 2 ... QxQ; 3 RxR mate.

191   1 Q—K4 and wins
Protecting himself against the mate, Black succumbs to QxB.

192   1 Q—B5 and wins
Black can parry the mating threat only at the cost of giving up his Rook.

193   1 NxN   RxN
     2 R—R8ch   K—R2
     3 B—K4ch   Resigns
White wins the Rook.

194   1 P—K5   N—Q4
     2 BxPch   KxB
     3 NxN   BxN
     4 Q—Q3ch   ....
White wins the Bishop.

195   1 BxP!   PxB
     2 Q—N4ch and wins
White forks King and Knight.

196   1 Q—B3!   Resigns
White wins a piece.

197   1 RxP!   RxR
     2 BxRch   KxB
     3 Q—B4ch and wins
White forks King and Bishops.

198   1 N—N5!   N—B3
If 1 ... BxN; 2 QxRP mate. If 1 ... QxB; 2 BxPch, K—R1; 3 NxBP mate.
     2 BxPch   K—R1
     3 NxBP mate

199 1 B—R6ch!   K—N1
If 1 . . . KxB; 2 Q—R5ch forces
mate. If 1 . . . K—R1; 2 N—B7ch
wins the Queen.
    2 NxN   BxN
    3 QxPch and wins
White continues 4 QxQB.

200 1 B—Q4!   R—KN1
If 1 . . . BxB; 2 QxBch wins the
Knight. If 1 . . . N—B5; 2 BxBch,
KxB; 3 Q—Q4ch forks King and
Knight.
    2 BxBch   RxB
    3 Q—Q4   R—QN1
    4 R—N1   Q—N2
    5 B—N3 and wins
White has trapped the Knight.

201 1 N—R7!   RxN
If 1 . . . Q—B2; 2 R—K8ch wins.
    2 P—Q8/Qch   BxQ
    3 QxBch   K—N2
    4 BxN   PxB
    5 Q—Q4ch   ....
White wins the Rook.

202 1 P—B6!   PxP
If 1 . . . NxP; 2 Q—N8ch etc.
    2 BxN   RxB
    3 Q—N4ch and wins
White wins a Rook.

203 1 N—Q8ch!   ....
Not 1 QxR, QxN; 2 QxB, QxR.
    1 ....   QxN
    2 QxRch   K—B1
    3 QxB and wins

204 1 RxB!   RxR
If 1 . . . QxQ; 2 RxRch!
    2 Q—K8ch and wins
White forces mate.

205 1 P—KB4   B—Q3
    2 P—K5   B—B4ch
    3 K—R1   N—N1
    4 Q—Q5 and wins
This "triple attack" wins because
of the mate threat.

206 1 P—KB4   B—Q3
    2 Q—K8ch   ....
White wins the Rook.

207 1 RxNch   PxR
    2 QxPch   ....
White wins the Rook.

208 1 RxBch   KxR
    2 Q—Q4ch   ....
White wins the Rook.

209 1 BxB   RxB
    2 Q—Q3   ....
White wins a piece.

210 1 RxB   NxR
    2 Q—R4ch and wins
After 3 QxN White has two pieces
for a Rook.

211 1 RxB   RxR
    2 Q—B6   ....
White wins a Rook.

212 1 P—KR3!   N—R3
    2 Q—K4   ....
Wins the Rook; Black must guard
against QxP mate.

213 1 R—N5ch!   N—N3
    2 Q—K6ch   ....
White wins the Bishop.

214 1 BxN   QxB
    2 Q—Q5ch   ....
White wins the Knight.

215 1 N—N5!   PxN
If 1 . . . R—KB3; 2 QxB, QxQ;
3 NxQ wins a piece.
    2 QxNPch and wins
After 3 QxRch White is the Exchange ahead.

216 1 NxQP!   PxN
    2 RxN!   QxR
    3 Q—K8!   ....
Threatens 4 Q—KR8 mate.
    3 ....   R—B1
    4 NxRch   QxN
Else White mates.
    5 QxQ   Resigns

217 1 NxP!   NxN
    2 Q—R5ch   N—N3
    3 Q—Q5 and wins
White's mate threat enables him
to win the Rook.

218 1 BxB   KxB
Or 1 . . . R—K1; 2 B—K5, P—
B3; 3 Q—K4! remaining a piece
ahead.
    2 Q—K5ch   N—B3
    3 R—Q6!   ....
White wins the Knight.

219 1 Q—B7!   R/N1—Q1
     2 BxN and wins
Black cannot recapture.

220 1 NxN   BxN
     2 BxB   RxB
     3 Q—Q5ch   ....
White wins the Queen Rook.

221 1 BxN   PxB
No better is 1 . . . QxB.
     2 Q—R3ch   ...
White wins the Bishop.

222 1 P—Q5   N—K2
     2 Q—R4ch and wins

223 1 N—R6ch!   PxN
     2 Q—N4ch and wins
White's next is 3 QxR.

224 1 R—R3!   P—R3
White threatened 2 RxPch!, KxR;
3 Q—R5 mate. If 1 . . . P—KN3;
2 PxP!, RxP; 3 RxPch!, KxR; 4
Q—R5ch, R—R3; 5 Q—B7ch followed by mate.
     2 Q—Q2! and wins
White threatens 3 QxB as well as
3 QxPch! (or 3 RxPch!), PxQ; 4
RxP mate.

225 1 NxB   RxN
     2 P—B4 and wins

226 1 BxPch!   RxB
If 1 . . . KxB; 2 Q—N3ch wins
the Bishop.
     2 PxP   N—N5
Black dare not play . . . NxP??
losing his Queen.
     3 P—K6   ....
The double attack wins back a
piece.

227 1 P—K3   N—B4
Or 1 . . . N—N4; 2 Q—R4.
     2 Q—N4 and wins

228 1 P—B6   RxP
If 1 . . . R—N1; 2 Q—Q6ch wins.
     2 Q—Q8ch   Resigns
White wins the Rook.

229 1 Q—K7ch   KxN
     2 P—KN4ch   Resigns

230 1 RxN   PxRch
     2 KxP   Resigns
White threatens KxR and also
P—B6ch.

231 1 P—B6ch   KPxP
     2 P—K7   Resigns

232 1 BxN   KxB
     2 P—B5   PxP
     3 PxP   Q—QB3
     4 P—B6ch and wins

233 1 P—B3   Q—R5
     2 QxQ   PxQ
     3 P—K4 and wins

234 1 BxPch!   NxB
     2 R—Q7ch   K—B1
     3 NxNch   K—N1
     4 N—B8 dis ch   ....
White mates next move.

235 1 P—Q7   R—Q1
     2 Q—R5 and wins
White wins a piece.

236 1 RxB!   KxR
If 1 . . . QxR; 2 B—B6 wins the
Queen.
     2 B—B6ch!   QxB
     3 N—R5ch   Resigns
White wins the Queen.

237 1 N—K8!   Q—K2
     2 Q—KN3   QxN
White threatened mate.
     3 QxR and wins

238 1 NxN   QxN
     2 BxPch   Resigns
White wins the Queen.

239 1 QxPch!!   KxQ
Or 1 . . . RxQ; 2 RxQch and 3
RxB.
     2 RxRch   QxR
     3 N—B5ch and wins
White is a piece up after 4 NxR.

240 1 P—N5!   PxP
Forced.
     2 RxN!   RxR
     3 RxR   QxR
     4 Q—B8ch and wins
White wins the Rook.

241 1 RxB!   RxR
     2 Q—Q4   Q—K4
     3 R—K1!   Resigns
If 3 . . . QxQ; 4 RxR mate. If 3
. . . QxR; 4 Q—N7 mate.

242 1 R—B5   ....
White wins a piece.

243   1 B—B7!!   KxB

If 1 . . . QxB; 2 RxR winning the Exchange as Black's Bishop is pinned. If 1 . . . RxR; 2 QxNPch, K—B1; 3 Q—N8ch, K—K2; 4 Q—K8ch, K—Q3; 5 Q—K6 mate.

     2 RxR   QxR
     3 Q—N7ch   ....

White wins the Rook.

244   1 Q—KR8ch   K—N4
     2 Q—K5ch and wins

(2 Q—Q8ch also wins the Bishop.)

245   1 NxP!   PxN
     2 Q—N5ch   ....

White wins back the sacrificed material and remains a Pawn ahead.

246   1 P—Q5!   BxP
     2 NxBP   ....

White wins the Exchange.

247   1 RxB!   RxR
     2 RxR   QxR
     3 Q—KN4ch   ....

White wins the Rook.

248   1 N—R4!   BxN
     2 P—Q6!   ....

This secondary threat explains the previous move.

     2 ....   PxP
     3 RxR   N—B3
     4 BxR   RxB
     5 PxB   ....

White has won the Exchange.

249   1 RxB!   RxR
     2 Q—K5   ....

The threat of 3 QxNP mate wins the Rook.

250   1 Q—Q4   P—B3
     2 NxB   RxN
     3 QxR   QxB
     4 R—K1   ....

White has won the Exchange.

251   1 B—R6   NxQ
     2 BxPch   K—N1
     3 BxN dis ch B—N4
     4 RxB mate

252   1 NxP!   PxN
     2 BxN   PxB
     3 RxR!   RxR
     4 Q—N3ch   ....

This is the point. White continues 5 QxR with a Pawn ahead.

253   1 ....   P—Q6!
     2 RxP   RxR
     3 QxR   P—K5
     4 BxN   PxB

Black wins a piece.

254   1 ....   B—B3

Black wins a piece.

255   1 ....   QxQ
     2 RxQ   B—N5
     3 R—Q1   R—B7

Black wins a piece.

256   1 ....   P—KN4
     2 B—K3   P—N5

Black wins a piece.

257   1 ....   RxN!
     2 RxR   NxP!
     Resigns

For if 3 BxN, QxRch and Black mates next move.

258   1 ....   Q—K3!
     2 Q—B2   RxPch!
     3 KxR   Q—R3 mate

259   1 ....   Q—B3 and wins

260   1 ....   R—KN6ch and wins

261   1 ....   R—K1!
     2 Q—KB4   Q—Q5!

Black wins a piece.

262   1 ....   KNxKP!
     2 NxN   Q—R5ch and wins

After 3 . . . QxB or 3 . . . BxB, depending on White's reply, Black is a Pawn ahead.

263   1 ....   RxPch!!
     2 QxR   B—N3ch
     3 Q—K4   ....

If 3 K—B3 or 3 K—B4, R—B7 mate.

     3 ....   BxQch

Black is the Exchange ahead.

264   1 ....   BxB
     2 KxB   Q—KN8

Black wins a piece.

265   1 ....   NxBP!
     2 KxN   NxN
     3 BxN   Q—R5ch

Black continues 4 . . . QxB.

266
1 ....   RxQP!
2 RxR   Q—R6ch
3 K—N1   QxRPch
4 K—B1   Q—R8ch
Followed by 5 . . . QxR/Q5 and wins.

267
1 ....   BxN
2 PxB   RxB!
3 PxR   QxPch
Black wins the Rook.

268
1 ....   QxRch!
2 NxQ   RxQ
3 PxR   R—Q8ch
Black wins the Knight.

269
1 ....   P—B3
2 B—B4   Q—R4ch
Black wins the Knight.

270
1 ....   Q—B2ch!
2 P—N3   Q—K2!
Black wins the Rook because of the simultaneous threat of . . . Q—K7 mate.

271
1 ....   BxPch!
2 KxB   NxP
3 Q—K2   NxB
4 QxN   BxN
5 QxB   Q—R5ch
Black wins the Rook.

272
1 ....   Q—K8ch
2 R—Q1   Q—K5!
Threatens mate.
3 R—Q3   Q—R8ch!
4 R—Q1   QxP and wins
Black still threatens mate and thus gains time to pick up the remaining White Pawn.

273
1 ....   BxN
2 PxB   NxKP!
3 PxN   QxPch and wins
Black continues 4 . . . QxB/Q6.

274
1 ....   BxPch!
2 KxB   Q—N5ch
If now 3 K—R1, Q—B6 mate.
3 K—B1   QxRch
If now 4 R—K1, Q—B6ch forcing checkmate.
4 K—N2   Q—N5ch
5 K—B1   Q—B6ch
6 K—K1   QxRch
Black wins the Bishop too.

275
1 ....   RxBch!
2 PxR   QxKPch
Black wins the Rook.

276 If Black tries to win a piece by the double attack 1 . . . Q—K4? he fails after 2 N—B3! The right way is:
1 ....   RxN!
2 RxR   Q—K4!
Black wins the Rook because of the threat . . . Q—R7 mate.

277
1 ....   RxN!
2 PxR   B—Q5ch
Black wins the Rook.

278
1 ....   NxQP!
2 PxN   Q—R5ch
Black continues 3 . . . QxB.

279
1 ....   R—Q4!
2 B—B4   ....
After 2 B—K8 Black has the same winning move.
2 ....   P—QN4 and wins

280
1 ....   P—K6!
Threatens . . . P—K7.
2 R—K1   PxP
Black wins a piece.

281
1 ....   P—N3!
2 Q—R4   BxKBPch!
3 KxB   P—N4ch
Black wins the Queen and comes out a Rook ahead.

282
1 ....   P—KN4!
2 B—N3   P—N5
If the attacked Knight moves, 3 . . . N—K5 wins a piece.
3 P—QR3   PxN!
4 PxB   PxP
The double attack wins a piece.

283
1 ....   P—Q5!
Threatens 2 . . . QxQch! 3 KxQ, P—Q6ch winning a piece.
2 QxQ   PxQ
Black wins a piece, for if 3 N moves, P—Q7ch wins the Rook.

284
1 ....   NxPch!
2 PxN   Q—Q5ch
3 K—R1   RxR and wins

285
1 ....   RxB
2 RxR   BxPch
Black continues 3 . . . BxR.

286 1 .... Q—B5!
This wins a piece, as White cannot guard both Rook and Knight.

287 1 .... Q—N3!!
Threatening . . . QxP mate and also attacking White's Bishop. White can stop the mate only by losing his Bishop. Instead this follows:
2 BxQ N—K7 mate!

288 1 .... NxBch
Forcing White's reply.
2 QxN Q—Q5ch and wins
Black continues 3 . . . QxN/B6.

289 1 .... RxBP!
If now 2 RxR, RxPch; 3 PxR, BxRch; 4 QxB, QxQch and 5 . . . QxR. If 2 PxR, RxPch and mate next move.
2 B—R2 RxP!
3 PxR/R3 RxR mate

290 1 .... Q—R6!!
Threatening not only . . . QxB but also . . . N—N6ch and mate next move.
2 PxQ N—B7 dbl ch
3 K—N1 NxP mate

291 1 .... R—Q6
2 QR—B1 ....
White can stop mate only by losing his Bishop
2 .... R—R6 mate

292 1 .... PxP!
2 R—Q2 PxP dis ch
If now 3 K—N2, R—KR6! saves everything for Black.
3 KxP B—B2!!
Black wins, for if 4 BxR, BxPch and 5 . . . BxR.

293 1 .... Q—K2!
Attacking the Rook and also threatening . . . Q—K8 mate.
2 P—KR4 Q—K8ch
3 K—R2 QxPch
Black continues 4 . . . QxR.

294 1 .... P—B4
2 N—B3 P—B5 and wins

295 White's discovered attack wins the Queen because of the threat 2 Q—R8 mate:
1 N—Q5! Resigns

296 White's discovered attack wins the Queen or forces checkmate:
1 N—K6! QxB
2 N—Q5! Q—K5
3 N/Q5—B7 mate

297 1 RxPch! ....
If now 1 . . . PxR; 2 B—N6ch wins the Queen. Or 1 . . . BxR; 2 B—N5ch with the same result. So Black must move his King, remaining with a decidedly inferior game.

298 1 B—K7! R—K1
2 B—N4 Resigns
By threatening mate, White wins the Queen.

299 1 QxR QxQ
2 P—B8/Q dis ch Resigns

300 1 B—R6! R—N1?
This loses a whole Rook instead of "only" the Exchange.
2 B—B4ch ....
White wins a whole Rook.

301 1 NxN! QxQ
Or 1 . . . QxN; 2 Q—N7 mate.
2 NxNch K—R1
3 N—B7 mate

302 1 NxB! Resigns
If 1 . . . RxN; 2 QxR; or 1 . . . RxQ; 2 NxQch and White wins a Rook in either event.

303 1 N—N5! QxN
2 BxB and wins

304 1 RxN! NxR
2 RxN ....
If now 2 . . . QxR; 3 N—R6ch wins the Queen.

305 1 P—Q6! BxB
2 PxB R—K1
3 KxB PxN
4 PxP RxP
5 P—N6! ....
White will win the Queen Rook Pawn and Queen Pawn, but aside from that, his far advanced passed Pawn assures him an easy win.

306 1 Q—N4 P—N3
2 N—R6ch Resigns

307 1 P—KB3 B—R4
2 P—KB4! ....

If 2 . . . BxB; 3 PxN or 2 . . .
PxP; 3 BxB. White wins a piece in
either event.

308 1 N—K6!   Q—R4ch
If 1 . . . QxB; 2 N/N5—B7 mate.
    2 B—Q2   QxBch
    3 QxQ   NxQ
    4 N/N5—B7 mate

309 1 B—B4!   RxRch
If 1 . . . QxB; 2 RxRch etc.
    2 BxR!   Q—R4
    3 R—K1!   Resigns
If the Bishop moves, 4 Q—K8ch!
decides.

310 1 NxBP!   QxN
Else his Rook goes lost.
    2 BxPch   Resigns
White wins the Queen.

311 1 PxP   BxP
Or 1 . . . NxQBP; 2 BxN win-
ning a piece.
    2 BxB   NxB
    3 RxN!   Resigns
If 3 . . . QxR/B4; 4 RxRch etc.

312 1 N—K6ch!   QxN
    2 Q—R5ch   K—N1
If 2 . . . K—B3; 3 P—N5 mate.
Or 2 . . . P—N3; 3 Q—R7ch, K—
B3; 4 QxP mate.
    3 B—R7ch   K—R1
    4 B—N6 dis ch K—N1
    5 Q—R7 mate

313 1 N—N5!   R—Q1
If 1 . . . QxQ; 2 NxP/B7 mate!
    2 QxQ   RxQ
    3 NxP/B7ch   K—N1
    4 P—R5   Resigns
The Rook is trapped, leaving
Black with a lost ending.

314 1 B—Q5!   Resigns
If 1 . . . RxR; 2 Q—N8 mate. If
1 . . . RxB; 2 RxR mate or 1 . . .
QxB; 2 RxRch followed by mate.

315 1 N—N5!   BxN
    2 BxB   NxPch
    3 RxN   . . . .
White continues 4 BxR.

316 1 Q—K6ch!   K—R2
No better is 1 . . . K—R4
    2 N—B6ch   PxN
    3 QxQ   Resigns

317 1 BxPch!   KxB
    2 QxQ   Resigns

318 1 N—Q5!   NxN
If 1 . . . QxQ; 2 NxNch wins a
piece.
    2 QxQ   NxQ
    3 BxB!   QN—Q2
    4 BxR   KxB
    5 P—K5   N—Q4
    6 BxN   PxB
    7 P—K6 and wins

319 1 BxN!   PxB
    2 NxP/B6ch! BxN
    3 RxNch!   Resigns
White continues 4 QxQ.

320 1 RxP!   QxKB
    2 B—B5!   QxQ
Expecting 3 RxQ??, R—Q8ch
and Black forces mate.
    3 RxBch!   QxR
    4 RxQ mate

321 1 N—B6!!   Resigns
No matter how Black plays he is
checkmated. For example: 1 . . .
NxQ; 2 RxP mate. Or 1 . . . PxN;
2 QxRP mate. Or 1 . . . P—R3;
2 Q—R7 mate.

322 1 P—Q5!   Resigns
In saving his Queen, Black loses
his Knight.

323 1 NxP!   BxQ
"Best" is 1 . . . PxN; 2 QxB and
White wins easily.
    2 BxPch   K—K2
    3 N—Q5 mate

324 1 N—Q5!   Q—R5
    2 B—N5ch!   QxB
    3 NxPch   Resigns
Black loses his Queen.

325 1 RxN!   QxR
    2 NxP   Q—B1
    3 BxB   QxB
    4 N—N6!   B—B3
    5 N—K7ch!   K—R1
    6 QxB!   PxQ
    7 BxP mate

326 1 P—B7 dis ch K—R2
On 1 . . . B—N2 White makes
a new Queen.
    2 Q—B5ch   K—R1
    3 Q—B6ch   K—R2

```
          4 P—N6ch      Resigns       336   1 ....          NxP!
     Black loses his Queen.                  2 QxQ            NxRch
                                             3 K—B1          BxQ
327   1 N—N6!        R—R2                    4 KxN           RxN
      2 N/B3xB       QxN                     Resigns
      3 NxB          RxN
      4 BxPch        Resigns          337   1 ....          NxN
     White wins a whole Rook.               2 QxN           N—N5ch!
                                            Resigns
328   1 QxN!!        QxQ               White loses his Queen.
      2 P—QB4        Q—Q2
      3 RxPch        K—R1             338   1 ....          NxP!
      4 R—N8 dbl ch  KxR                   If now 2 BxB, N—Q6ch followed
      5 R—N1ch       Q—N5              by . . . QxB. If 2 PxN, BxB etc.
      6 RxQ mate
                                      339   1 ....          QxR!
329   1 N—Q6        R—K2                    2 RxQ           RxN
      If 1 . . . R—B1 White wins the        3 RxR           RxR
     Exchange in the same way. But if        4 Q—R3          ....
     1 . . . R—KN1?; 2 N—D7 mate!           After 4 Q—R1 Black wins the
      2 NxB         ....              Queen the same way.
     White wins the Exchange by 3           4 ....          RxPch
     BxR etc.                               5 K—R1          RxP dis ch
                                            Resigns
330   1 RxB!        QxR                White loses his Queen.
      2 N—KN6!      Resigns
      If 2 . . . QxQ; 3 N/Q5—K7 mate. 340   1 ....          N—K6
                                           Forcing White's reply.
331   1 ....        BxN!                    2 R—K1          N—B5ch!
      2 QxR         N—K4                     3 BxN           RxR and wins
     Threatens . . . Q—N5.
      3 K—R1        BxNPch!           341   1 ....          BxQP!
      4 KxB         Q—N5ch!                 2 QxB           BxPch!
      5 K—R1        Q—K5ch                  3 NxB           RxQ
      6 K—N1        N—B6ch                  Resigns
      7 K—N2 N—R5 dbl ch
      8 K—N3        Q—N7ch            342   1 ....          NxBP!
      9 KxN         B—K2ch                  2 KxN           BxNPch
     And Black mates next move.             Resigns
                                      White loses his Queen.
332   1 ....        N—Q6!
      2 R—Q1        Q—R8ch            343   1 ....          Q—B8ch
      3 K—K2        N—B5ch!                 2 K—R2          Q—B5ch
      Resigns                              If now 3 K—N1, N—B6ch wins
      If 4 PxN, QxRch; 5 K—K3, Q—     White's Queen.
     Q6 mate. If 4 K—B3, QxNPch wins        3 K—R1          Q—KB8ch
     the Queen.                             4 K—R2          QxR and wins

333   1 ....        B—K6!             344   1 ....          P—Q6!
      Resigns                              If now 2 QxP, QxB etc.
     Black threatens mate as well as        2 BxQ           PxQ and wins
     . . . BxBch.                     White loses his Rook or Bishop.

334   1 ....        RxKP!             345   1 ....          B—KR6!
      2 QxR         Q—B6ch                  2 QxR           B—QB4ch
      3 Q—B2        QxQ mate                If now 3 R/K4—Q4, BxRch; 5
                                      RxB, Q—K8 mate.
335   1 ....        N—B2                     3 K—R1          BxPch!
      Resigns                               4 KxB           Q—N5ch
     White must lose the Knight or the
     Bishop.
```

If now 5 K—R1, Q—B6 mate.
5 K—B1   Q—B6ch
6 K—K1   Q—B7 mate

346   1 ....   N—KB6ch!
If now 2 K—R1, NxR wins.
2 PxN   Q—N3ch
3 K—R1   N—N6ch!
4 RPxN   QxQ
Resigns

347   1 ....   RxBch!
2 KxR   B—Q6ch!
Resigns
White loses his Queen.

348   1 ....   N—KN6!
2 QxQ   N/Q5—K7 mate

349   1 QxRch!   KxQ
2 B—B2 dis ch! and wins
White continues 3 BxQ.

350   1 B—R7ch   K—R1
2 B—N8 dis ch!   KxB
Or 2 . . . B—R3; 3 Q—R7 mate.
3 Q—R7 mate

351   1 N—B7!!   Q—B3
If 1 . . . KxN; 2 PxP dis ch wins
Black's Queen.
2 PxP and wins
Black cannot save his Queen,
Rook, and Bishop.

352   1 NxP!   RxQ
If 1 . . . NxB; 2 N—N5 dis ch,
K—R3; 3 RxP mate.
2 NxR dis ch   K—B3
3 NxQ and wins
White comes out the Exchange
ahead.

353   1 RxN!   PxR
2 QxRch!   KxQ
3 PxP dis ch and wins
White continues 4 PxQ.

354   1 QxNch!   K—K2
If 1 . . . KxN; 2 N—B6 dis ch
and mate.
2 N—Q6   Resigns

355   1 R—Q7ch   R—B2
2 RxRch   KxR
3 B—B8 dis ch   ....
White continues 4 BxB.

356   1 R—KR1   ....
Threatens 2 K—N2 dis ch and
mate.

1 ....   K—R4
2 K—N3 dis ch   ....
White wins the Bishop.

357   1 Q—Q5   ....
Threatening a discovered check—
such as R—B6 dis ch.
1 ....   Q—B8ch
If 1 . . . K—R1; 2 Q—Q8ch and
mate next move.
2 R—B1 dis ch Resigns

358   1 Q—B5ch   R—K2
2 N—N6ch!   KxB
If 2 . . . PxN; 3 R—R8ch, KxB;
4 PxN dis ch, K—K3; 5 R—K1ch
and White mates soon.
3 PxN dis ch   K—N1
If 3 . . . KxN; 4 Q—B5 mate.
4 NxRch   K—R1
5 N—N6ch   K—N1
6 Q—B8ch!   RxQ
7 RxR mate

359   1 P—Q5 dis ch Resigns

360   1 B—R5ch!   P—N3
2 NxNP!   N—N3
If 2 . . . PxN; 3 BxP mate.
3 N—K5 mate

361   1 BxN   NxB
2 BxP dis ch   K—Q2
3 BxB   Resigns
If 3 . . . RxB; 4 N—K5ch wins
the Bishop.

362   1 NxPch!   BxN
2 RxB   BxB
3 RxPch   K—R1
4 RxP dis ch   K—N1
5 R—KN7ch   K—R1
6 R—QB7disch K—N1
7 RxB   Resigns

363   1 RxB!   QxR
2 BxPch   K—N1
3 P—B5 dis ch   ....
White continues 4 PxQ.

364   1 QxPch!   KxQ
2 PxP dis ch   K—N3
3 PxP   ....
White plays 4 PxR/Q, leaving
him a whole Rook ahead.

365   1 R—R8ch!   KxR
2 P—K6 dis ch   Q—N2
3 BxQch   Resigns
Black has only two pieces for
the Queen.

216 · SOLUTIONS ·

366 White wins the Queen:
1 N—B5 dis ch   Resigns

367 1 Q—R5ch!   K—N2
If 1 . . . KxQ; 2 N—B7 dis ch,
B—N4; 3 RxB mate.
2 Q—R7ch   K—B1
3 QxR   N—K2
4 RxBch   QxR
5 N—R7ch   Resigns
White wins the Queen.

368 1 N—R5   PxN
2 BxPch   K—R1
3 B—N6 dis ch   K—N1
4 Q—R7ch   K—B1
5 B—R6ch   K—K2
6 QxPch   K—Q1
7 QxR mate

369 1 R—N3ch!   PxR
2 BxPch!   KxB
3 RPxP dis ch   K—N1
4 R—R8 mate

370 1 R—K7!   BxN
2 RxPch   K—R1
3 RxB dis ch   K—N1
4 RxB   Resigns

371 1 RxNch   KxR
2 NxP dis ch and wins

372 1 Q—R8ch   N—N1
2 QxPch!   KxQ
3 BxB dis ch   K—R1
4 RxNch!   KxR
5 R—N1ch   K—R1
6 B—B6 mate

373 1 R—K7!   K—N1
If 1 . . . QxR; 2 P—B6 dis ch
wins the Queen.
2 RxRP and wins

374 1 QxRPch!   BxQ
2 P—B7 dis ch   P—K4
3 BxP mate

375 1 N—N6ch!   PxN
2 PxNP dis ch and wins

376 1 QxPch!   QxQ
2 RxQch   KxR
3 R—R1ch   B—R7
4 RxBch   K—N2
5 B—R6ch   K—R2
6 BxR mate

377 1 R—N7ch   K—B1
2 RxQP dis ch   K—N1
3 R—KN7ch   K—B1
4 R—N7 dis ch   K—N1
5 RxRch   N—B1
6 RxN mate

378 1 QxPch!   KxQ
2 R—QR3ch   K—N2
3 B—R6ch   K—R1
4 B—B8 mate

379 1 QxPch!   KxQ
2 B—R5ch!   KxR
3 B—B7 mate

380 1 B—B8 dis ch   B—R4
2 QxBch!   PxQ
3 R—R6 mate

381 1 NxNP!   KxN
2 QxPch!   KxQ
3 BxN mate

382 1 P—N4!   N—B5
If 1 . . . N—B3; 2 B—Q5 dis ch
wins the Knight.
2 BxN dis ch and wins

383 1 N—K6 dis ch!   PxQ
2 B—N7 mate

384 1 QxRP!   PxQ
2 PxP dis ch   K—B1
3 R—N8ch!   KxR
4 P—R7ch   K—B1
5 P—R8/Q mate

385 1 . . . .   BxN!
2 RxR   P—K7 dis ch
3 K—R1   P—K8/Q mate

386 1 . . . .   QxB!
So that if 2 QxQ, R—K8ch, 3
B—B1, RxBch!; 4 RxR, P—B7
mate.
2 Q—B1   Q—N7!
3 Q—B1   QxR!
4 QxQ   R—K8ch!
5 QxR   P—B7 dis ch
Black mates in two moves.

387 1 . . . .   N—Q5 dis ch!
2 N—Q2   RxNch
3 RxR   N—B6ch
Followed by 4 . . . NxR.

388 1 . . . .   N—R5 dis ch
If now 2 K—N1, Q—KN5 mate.
2 K—K1   NxN mate

389　　1 ....　　　　　　NxP!
　　　　2 QxN　　　　　QxQch
　　　　3 KxQ　　　　　P—B6 dis ch
　　　　4 NxB　　　　　PxR! and wins

390　　1 ....　　　　　　N—N6ch!
　　　　2 PxN　　　　　PxP dis ch
　　　　3 BxR　　　　　Q—R5 mate

391　　1 ....　　　　　　RxNPch!
　　　　2 KxR　　　　　RxPch!
　　　　3 BxR　　　　　P—K6 dis ch
　　　　　　Resigns
　　If 4 R—Q5 (forced), QxBch; 5
　K—R1, QxRch; 6 K—N2, Q—B7ch;
　7 K—R1, P—K7 and wins.

392　　1 ....　　　　　　QxRch!
　　　　2 KxQ　　　　　N—B4 dis ch
　　Followed by 3 ... NxQ.

393　　1 ....　　　　　　QxB!
　　　　2 PxQ　　　　　R—Q1 dis ch
　　Followed by 3 ... RxQ.

394　　1 ....　　　　　　QxN!
　　　　2 BxQ　　　　　P—K6 dis ch
　　　　3 Q—N2　　　　....
　　If 3 Q—B3, BxQch; 4 RxB, NxP;
　5 R—Q1, NxB; 6 RxN, B—B4 with
　a winning endgame.
　　　　3 ....　　　　　BxQch
　　　　4 KxB　　　　　NxP
　　　　5 R—R4　　　　....
　　If 5 R—Q1, RxN!; 6 BxR, P—K7
　and wins.
　　　　5 ....　　　　　KR—Q1
　　　　6 B—N6　　　　R—Q7ch
　　　　7 K—B3　　　　RxN!
　　　　8 PxR　　　　　P—K7 and wins

395　　1 ....　　　　　　P—K7 dis ch
　　Black wins, for if 2 R—B2,
　QxRch etc.

396　　1 ....　　　　　　RxKNP!
　　　　2 PxQ　　　　　RxRch
　　　　3 BxR　　　　　R—Q7 dis ch
　　　　4 K—N1　　　　B—Q5ch
　　　　5 B—B2　　　　RxRch
　　　　6 Q—K1　　　　RxQ mate

397　　1 QxPch!　　　　KxQ
　　　　2 BxP dbl ch　　K—N3
　　If 2 ... K—K2; 3 R—B7 mate.
　　　　3 B—B7ch　　　KxP
　　　　4 B—B1ch　　　K—N5
　　　　5 R—B4ch　　　K—N4
　　　　6 P—R4ch　　　K—R3
　　　　7 R—B6 mate

398　　1 Q—R5ch!　　　NxQ
　　　　2 PxP dbl ch　　K—N3
　　　　3 B—B2ch　　　K—N4
　　　　4 R—B5ch　　　K—N3
　　If 4 ... K—N5; 5 P—R3ch leads
　to quick mate. Likewise if 4 ...
　K—R5; 5 R—K4ch etc.
　　　　5 R—B6 dbl ch　K—N4
　　　　6 R—N6ch　　　K—R5
　　　　7 R—K4ch　　　N—B5
　　　　8 RxNch　　　　K—R4
　　　　9 P—N3!　　　　....
　　Followed by 10 R—R4 mate.

399　　1 Q—Q8ch!　　　KxQ
　　　　2 B—R5 dbl ch　K—K1
　　　　3 R—Q8 mate

400　　1 NxBP!　　　　PxN
　　　　2 N—B6ch!　　　QxN
　　　　3 Q—Q8ch!　　　BxQ
　　　　4 B—N5 mate

401　　1 Q—Q7ch!　　　BxQ
　　　　2 N—Q6 dbl ch　K—Q1
　　　　3 N—B7ch　　　K—B1
　　　　4 R—K8ch!　　　BxR
　　　　5 R—Q8 mate

402　　1 N—K7 dbl ch　K—R1
　　　　2 N—N6ch!　　　PxN
　　　　3 RPxN dis ch　Q—R5
　　　　4 RxQ mate

403　　1 NxP!　　　　　N—K2
　　If 1 ... either NxN; 2 RxNch
　is deadly.
　　　　2 NxN!　　　　　QxQ
　　　　3 N—B6 dbl ch　K—B1
　　　　4 BxN mate

404　　1 BxP!　　　　　BxR
　　　　2 BxP dbl ch! Resigns
　　If 2 ... KxB; 3 Q—K6 mate.
　Or 2 ... K—Q1; 3 Q—K8ch win-
　ning Black's Queen.

405　　1 Q—Q8ch!　　　KxQ
　　　　2 B—KN5dblch　K—K1
　　　　3 R—Q8 mate

406　　1 Q—Q8ch!　　　KxQ
　　　　2 B—KN5dblch　K—K1
　　Or 2 ... K—B2; 3 B—Q8 mate.
　　　　3 R—Q8 mate

407　　1 RxNP!　　　　PxR
　　　　2 Q—R7ch　　　N—Q2

218 · SOLUTIONS ·

If 2 . . . K—Q1; 3 Q—R8ch is decisive.

      3 BxN!   Q—N1

If 3 . . . QxB; 4 QxQch, KxQ; 5 RxR and White wins easily.

      4 R—N7ch!   KxR

If 4 . . . RxR; 5 QxQ and wins. Or 4 . . . K—Q1; 5 QxQch and wins.

      5 B—B8 dbl ch! and wins

The most beautiful double check ever played. After 5 . . . KxB; 6 QxQch White wins a Rook.

408   1 R—Q7!   QxR
       2 RxNPch!   KxR
       3 B—R6ch   K—R1
       4 N—N6ch!   PxN
       5 PxP   Q—B8ch
       6 K—R4   Q—B6
       7 B—N7 dbl ch KxB
       8 Q—R7 mate

409   1 Q—Q8ch!   KxQ
       2 B—KN5dblch K—K1
       3 R—Q8 mate

410   1 R—N8 dbl ch! KxR
       2 R—KN1 mate

411   1 N/Q2xN!   NxNch
       2 QxN!   QxQ
       3 N—B6 dbl ch K—Q1
       4 R K8 mate

412   1 B—Q6 dbl ch! KxB
       2 R—Q3   . . . .
White wins the Queen.

413   1 R—N8ch!   KxR
Or 1 . . . RxR; 2 NxQ etc.
       2 NxQ dbl ch Resigns
White wins the Black Queen without losing his own.

414   1 Q—Q7ch!   BxQ
       2 N—Q6 dbl ch K—Q1
       3 N—B7ch   K—B1
       4 R—K8ch!   BxR
       5 R—Q8 mate

415   1 . . . .   B—Q6 dbl ch
       2 K—K1   R—B8 mate

416   1 . . . .   R—B8 dbl ch!
       2 KxR   Q—B5ch
       3 K—Q2   Q—Q6ch
       4 K—K1   Q—K6ch
       5 K—B1   R—KB1
       Resigns

White is helpless; for example 6 Q—B3, B—R6ch etc.

417   1 . . . .   N—B6 mate!

418   1 . . . .   Q—N7ch!
       2 KxQ   RxNP mate

419   1 . . . .   QxR!
       2 PxQ   B—N5 dbl ch
       3 K—Q1   R—K8 mate

420   1 . . . .   RxBP!
       2 QxQ   RxN mate

421   1 Q—Q5ch!   Resigns
If 1 . . . RxQ; 2 RxR mate.
(If White plays 1 QxQ in the diagram position, Black can make a fight of it with 1 . . . N—B7 dbl ch or . . . N—B5 dis ch.)

422   1 N—Q5   Q—Q1
       2 BxP   Q—Q2
       3 Q—N4!   R—K3
If 3 . . . QxQ; 4 RxR mate.
       4 RxR   QxR
If 4 . . . PxR; 5 N—B6ch.
       5 N—B6ch   K—B1
If 5 . . . QxN; 6 QxBch and mate follows.
       6 B—Q6ch!   QxB
       7 QxBch   K—K2
       8 N—N8 mate

423   1 Q—B4!   Resigns
White threatens 2 Q—N8 mate, and if 1 . . . RxQ; 2 RxN mate.

424   1 R—Q7!   QxR
If 1 . . . NxR; 2 Q—KN4ch, K—R3; 3 R—B5 wins.
       2 QxNch   K—N3
       3 R—B5   Resigns
Black's King cannot escape.

425   1 RxPch!.   QxR
If 1 . . . KxR; 2 BxN, QxB; 3 R—KN1ch forcing mate.
       2 BxNch   R—B2
       3 R—KN1!   QxR
       4 QxRch   K—R1
       5 Q—R5ch   K—N2
       6 Q—R6 mate

426   1 R—B8ch!   QxR
       2 QxPch!   RxQ
       3 RxR mate

427 1 R—Q5ch!   NxR
If 1 . . . K—R3; 2 B—B8ch
wins.
2 B—K2ch   K—R4
3 R—QR7ch   R—R3
4 RxR mate

428 1 R—K5   Q—Q2
2 RxRch   QxR
3 P—Q7!   QxP
4 Q—N8ch   K—R2
5 Q—R8ch!   NxQ
6 R—N7 mate

429 1 B—R3!   QxB
2 Q—K6!   N—Q1
3 Q—B7ch!   NxQ
4 N—K6 mate

430 1 Q—R6!   Resigns
If 1 . . . BxQ; 2 N—K7 mate.

431 1 B—B6!   PxB
Or 1 . . . R—KN1; 2 QxNPch!,
RxQ; 3 R—Q8ch and mate follows.
2 KPxP   R—KN1
3 R—Q8!   QRxR
4 RxR   Resigns
White threatens mate, and if 4
. . . RxR; 5 Q—N7 mate.

432 1 Q—K7!   Q—B2
If 1 . . . RxQ; 2 R—B8 mate.
If 1 . . . RxR; 2 Q—N7 mate.
2 Q—B8ch!   RxQ
3 RxR mate

433 1 RxP!   Resigns
If 1 . . . RxR; 2 Q—Q8 mate;
if 1 . . . QxR; 2 Q—Q7 mate.

434 1 RxB!   Resigns
If 1 . . . R/N1xR; 2 RxR. Or 1
. . . R/R1xR; 2 RxR. In either case
White has won a piece.

435 1 BxP!   PxB
2 NxP   R—KN1
3 R—K8!   Resigns
If 3 . . . RxR; 4 Q—N7 mate. If
3 . . . QxR; 4 Q—B6ch and mate
next move.

436 1 RxB!   QxR
2 Q—N6   Resigns
There is no defense to the coming
3 QxRP mate.

437 1 R—QB5ch!   K—N1
If 1 . . . N—B2?; 2 QxQ. If 1
. . . R—B2; 2 RxRch, KxR; 3
RxPch with an easy win.
2 BxP!   RxB
If 2 . . . QxQch; 3 B—N2 dis ch!
and wins.
3 RxRch   KxR
4 Q—N2ch   K—N1
5 Q—N5ch   K—B2
6 Q—N7ch   K—Q3
7 R—Q5 mate

438 1 R—K8!   QxR
Or 1 . . . RxR; 2 Q—N7 mate.
2 Q—B6ch   R—N2
3 QxR mate

439 1 PxP!   NxQ
2 PxN dis ch   K—N1
3 R—R8ch!   KxR
4 P—B7!   B—K2
If 4 . . . Q—R5; 5 PxN/Qch and
mate next move.
5 R—R1ch   B—R5
6 P—B8/Q mate

440 1 R—KR3!   QxR
2 QxR mate

441 1 P—KB5!   Q—N4
If 1 . . . QxP; 2 BxP mate. If 1
. . . BxP; 2 BxPch, QxB; 3 RxR
mate.
2 BxPch!   QxB
3 P—B6   Q—N3
4 P—B7 dis ch   N—K4
5 RxN!   PxR
6 QxPch!   Resigns
If 6 . . . RxQ; 7 P—B8/Qch and
mate next move. If 6 . . . Q—N2;
7 QxRch, BxQ; 8 PxB/Qch, Q—
N1; 9 QxQ mate.

442 1 RxP!   RxR
2 NxP   Q—K2
3 NxR   QxN
4 Q—B4!   R—K2
5 P—B6!   . . . .
If now 5 . . . R—K3; 6 RxN!,
RxR; 7 P—B7 threatening 8 Q—B6
mate or 8 PxQ/Qch or 8 QxRch,
QxQ; 9 P—B8/Q mate.
5 . . . .   N—N3
6 RxR   NxR
7 P—B7!   Resigns
If 7 . . . Q—KB1; 8 Q—B6ch,
Q—N2; 9 P—B8/Qch and mate
next move.

443 1 Q—K8!   K—R4
If 1 . . . RxR; 2 Q—N5 mate.
          2 Q—B6!   Resigns
White wins the Black Rook, which
cannot move.

444 1 N—R6ch!   PxN
If 1 . . . K—R1; 2 NxPch wins
the Queen.
          2 BxN   Resigns
Black is helpless against the coming Q—KN3ch.

445 1 R—K8!   Resigns
If 1 . . . QxR; 2 Q—N7 mate.
Meanwhile Black is helpless against
a triple mate threat.

446 1 B—Q6!   Resigns
If 1 . . . QxB; 2 NxKBP mate.

447 1 R—K8ch!   RxR
If 1 . . . Q—B1; 2 QxRch leads
to mate.
          2 QxBch   K—R1
          3 QxRch   Q—B1
          4 QxQ mate

448 1 N—Q2!   P—Q3
If 1 . . . NxN; 2 R—N5 mate.
          2 NxN!   PxR
If 2 . . . NxN; 3 R—K8 mate.
          3 NxN mate

449 1 Q—K5!   Resigns
Black must lose the Queen, as
White threatens QxNP mate, and
if 1 . . . QxQ; 2 RxR mate.

450 1 N—R5!   PxN
If 1 . . . NxN; 2 QxRPch, K—B1;
3 QxBP mate.
          2 R—KN3   Resigns
There is no good move. If 2 . . .
P—R5; 3 N—K6 dis ch, PxR; 4
Q—N7 mate.
If 2 . . . B—KB1; 3 NxRP dis
ch, N—N5; 4 N—B6 mate.

451 1 RxNch   Resigns
If 1 . . . RxR; 2 RxRch followed
by 3 QxR with a piece ahead.
If 1 . . . QxR; 2 RxQch, KxR;
3 QxNch and wins.

452 1 RxN!   QxR
          2 Q—B3   Resigns
If 2 . . . Q—B3 or 2 . . . Q—K2
(to stop the threatened 3 Q—B7
mate), then 3 Q—Q5ch forces mate.

453 Black's Rooks are overworked.
He depends on the trap 1 RxB?,
RxR; 2 QxR, QxQ; 3 RxQ, R—
K8ch; 4 N—B1, N—K7ch; 5 K—
R1, RxN mate; but White is too
wily for him:
          1 QxB!   Resigns
Black loses at least a piece and
may get mated, for example 1 . . .
RxQ; 2 RxR mate. If 1 . . . QxQ;
2 R/Q1xQ! and if Black captures
either Rook, White mates.

454 1 QxRP!   QxQ
If 1 . . . R—B2; 2 QxR! winning
as in the main line.
          2 R—K8ch   B—B1
          3 B—Q4ch   Q—KN2
          4 RxB mate

455 1 Q—R5ch!   RxQ
          2 B—N6 mate

456 1 B—B6!   Resigns
White threatens 2 Q—R6 and 3
Q—N7 mate. Black cannot play 1
. . . NxB because of 2 Q—R8 mate.

457 1 . . . .   R—Q7!
          2 QxR   NxP
          Resigns
Black attacks the Queen and also
threatens . . . QxRP mate.

458 White expects to recover the
Exchange after 1 . . . RxRch; 2
QxR etc. But . . .
          1 . . . .   Q—Q2!
          Resigns
If 2 QxQ, RxR mate. If 2 Q—B4,
RxRch; 3 QxR, QxN and Black is
a Rook ahead.

459 1 . . . .   NxBch
          Resigns
White's Queen Knight is pinned,
so that after 2 QxN there follows 2
. . . QxRch.

460 1 . . . .   R—N3ch
          2 K—R2   Q—Q7ch!
          3 BxQ   R—B7ch
          4 Q—N2   RxQ mate

461 1 . . . .   N—B6!
          Resigns
If 2 BxN, RxN mate. On other
moves there follows 2 . . . RxNch!;
3 BxR, RxKRP mate.

• **SOLUTIONS** • 221

462 1 ....   R—K7!
              Resigns
Black threatens 2 . . . QxRP
mate or 2 . . . Q—N7 mate. If 2
RxR, QxR mate.

463 1 ....   R—K8ch!
              Resigns
If 2 QxR, QxN mate. If 2 NxR,
Q—R8 mate.

464 1 ....   P—N5!
         2 PxP   RxN!
         3 PxR   P—N6!
Threatens . . . P—N7 etc.
         4 PxP   P—B6ch!
If now 5 KxP, KxB wins.
         5 PxP   P—R6!
              Resigns
If 6 K—B1, KxB wins.

465 1 ....   RxBch
         2 RxR   QxR
Black has won a piece.

466 1 ....   B—Q4!
         2 Q—Q3   ....
If 2 N—K3, QxN wins a piece.
If 2 Q—K3, BxN; 3 KxB, N—Q4
with the same result.
Or 2 Q—KN3, BxN; 3 KxB, N—
R4 again winning a piece.
         2 ....   QxQ
         3 NxQ   BxN
         4 KxB   RxN
              Resigns
Black has won a piece.

467 1 ....   N—B4!
         2 NxN   RxBch
Followed by 3 . . . BxN and
Black has won a piece.

468 1 ....   RxN!
Winning a piece, for if 2 QxR,
QxP mate.

469 1 ....   Q—K4!
If now 2 QxQ, N—Q6ch and 3
. . . RxR mate.
         2 R—B4   N—Q6ch!
         3 K—N1   ....
Or 3 K—B2, QxQ etc.
         3 ....   QxQ
         4 RxQ   R—B8 mate

470 1 ....   NxP!
         2 PxN   QxNPch
If now 3 Q—KN2, BxNch wins.

         3 B—N2   B—R6
              Resigns
Black threatens 4 . . . BxNch,
and also . . . Q—R7ch. If 4 R—K2,
Q—R7ch; 5 K—B1, Q—R8ch is
murderous.

471 1 ....   N—K7!
If now 2 NxR Black wins as in
the main line. If 2 QxN, QxRch
wins.
         2 R/B1xP   RxPch!
         3 PxR   QxBch
         4 P—B3   QxPch
         5 K—R2   B—K4 mate

472 1 ....   R—Q5ch!
         2 QxR   Q—R7!
              Resigns
White has no satisfactory defense
against the threat of . . . Q—R7
mate.

473 1 ....   NxBch
         2 QxN   ....
White's Knight at Queen 2 is
pinned.
         2 ....   BxNch
Black has won a piece.

474 1 ....   R—QR4!
Also good is 1 . . . B—N6ch! win-
ning at least the Exchange.
         2 R—QR3   ....
If 2 R—Q8ch, B—K1 mate!
         2 ....   B—N6ch!
Because of the pin, Black wins a
piece.

475 1 PxP   QxP
If 1 . . . BxP; 2 BxN wins a
piece.
         2 NxB   QxN
         3 BxN and wins
White has won a piece.

476 1 B—R6ch   KxB
Or 1 . . . K—N3; 2 PxPch etc.
         2 QxKBP mate

477 1 P—KN4!   B—N3
         2 NxB and wins
White continues 3 QxN with a
piece ahead.

478 1 R—K8!   QxR
         2 BxNch   K—N1
         3 Q—R8 mate

222 · SOLUTIONS ·

479   1 RxP!   R—KR1
If 1 . . . RxR; 2 QxPch leads to mate.
     2 QxPch!   RxQ
     3 R—N8 mate

480   1 R—R7ch!   KxR
     2 QxPch   Resigns
White's R—KR1ch forces mate.

481   1 RxB!   QxR
     2 BxN and wins
White wins the Queen.

482   1 QxNch!   BxQ
     2 NxP mate

483   1 B—R3!   P—B3
Or 1 . . . QxB; 2 QxR etc.
     2 BxQ   PxQ
     3 BxN/R4 and wins
White is a Rook ahead.

484   1 R—B8ch!   RxR
Forced.
     2 QxQ   ....
White has won the Queen for a Rook.

485   1 R—R4   NxR/R5
If 1 . . . QxQ; 2 R/R5xP mate.
Or 1 . . . P—KR4; 2 RxNP dis ch, QxQ; 3 RxPch, N—R3; 4 R/R5xN mate.
     2 QxQ and wins

486   1 Q—KN4ch! Resigns
After 1 . . . QxQ; 2 RxRch and 3 PxQ White is a Rook ahead.

487   1 RxNch!   KxR
If 1 . . . QxR or . . . RxR; 2 QxP mate.
     2 N—N6ch!   PxN
     3 Q—R8ch   K—B2
     4 QxP mate

488   1 RxN!   PxR
     2 BxPch   K—N2
     3 Q—R5   Resigns
There is no good defense to the threat of 4 Q—R6ch, K—R1; 5 B—N6 dis ch, K—N1; 6 Q—R7 mate or 6 Q—R8 mate.

489   1 R—R7ch   K—R3
     2 RxNch   KxR
     3 QxR   ....
White has won a piece.

490   1 N—Q5   Q—Q1
     2 BxN   PxB
     3 NxB   ....
White has won a piece.

491   1 QxPch   K—B4
     2 R—B6ch   Resigns
White wins the Queen.

492   1 Q—Q8ch   R—K2
If 1 . . . K—B4; 2 P—N4 mate.
     2 N—Q7ch   Resigns
White wins the Rook.

493   1 RxN   ....
Or 1 BxN etc.
     1 ....   RxR
     2 BxR   QxB
     3 QxNPch   K—R2
     4 Q—R5ch   K—N2
     5 R—N3ch   K—B3
     6 Q—N5 mate

494   1 NxB   RxN
     2 QxN   Resigns
White has won a piece.

495   1 B—B5   RxRch
     2 QxR   Q—Q3
If 2 . . . QxB; 3 Q—K8 mate.
     3 Q—K8ch   Q—B1
     4 BxPch   Resigns
White wins the Queen.

496   1 NxP!   PxN
     2 P—K7   R—K1
     3 Q—K1!   Q—R3
If 3 . . . QxQ; 4 BxBP mate.
     4 Q—K3!   Q—R5
     5 Q—B4!   Resigns

497   1 NxNP!   PxN
     2 RxPch   K—B2
     3 RxNch   KxR
     4 QxR   ....
With two Pawns ahead plus the attack, White wins easily.

498   1 Q—B7!   Resigns
If 1 . . . QxQ; 2 BxNch wins a piece. If 1 . . . Q—N3; 2 QxB etc.

499   1 Q—R3!   Q—KB2
If 1 . . . QxQ; 2 BxBch wins a piece.
     2 BxBch   QxB
     3 QxP   ....
White has won a Pawn and has a winning attack.

500　1 Q—K6ch　　K—N2
　　　2 Q—K7ch　　Resigns
　　White wins the Knight.

501　1 R—K1!　　Resigns
　　Black cannot defend himself. If
　1 . . . RxR; 2 QxBch, K—K2; 3
　QxR and wins. If 1 . . . K—Q2; 2
　RxR wins at once.

502　1 QxRP!　　Resigns
　　If 1 . . . RxQ; 2 R—B8 mate.
　Black cannot meet the threats of
　2 QxR mate or 2 QxP mate or 2
　Q—B7 mate.

503　1 B—B8!　　BxB
　　　2 RxBch　　K—N2
　　　3 KxN　　Resigns
　　White has won a piece.

504　1 BxPch!　　QxB
　　　2 R—Q8ch　　KxR
　　　3 QxQ　　Resigns
　　White has all the play.

505　1 BxN!　　QxQ
　　　2 R—K1ch　　B—K2
　　　3 RxBch　　K—B1
　　　4 R—Q8 mate

506　1 RxB!　　QxR
　　　2 B—N5!　　Q—B1
　　If 2 . . . QxB; 2 B—B6 forces
　mate.
　　　3 BxR　　QxB
　　　4 B—B6　　Q—B1
　　　5 QxQch　　KxQ
　　　6 R—Q1　　Resigns
　　Only 6 . . . B—Q2 stops mate,
　but then 7 RxB leaves White a
　piece ahead.

507　1 R—K7!　　QxR
　　　2 QxRch　　Resigns
　　White wins the other Rook as
　well.

508　1 N—K6!　　NxN
　　If 1 . . . PxN; 2 Q—B8ch, K—
　R2; 3 Q—R6ch, K—N1; 4 R—B8
　mate.
　　　2 QxPch　　K—R1
　　　3 QxN/K6　　Resigns
　　White can win as he pleases.

509　1 R—K7!　　QxR
　　　2 NxB　　Q—B1
　　　3 RxPch!　　KxR

　　　4 Q—R5ch　　Q—R3
　　　5 QxQ mate

510　1 Q—B2ch　　Q—N3
　　If 1 . . . P—N3; 2 R—Q7ch,
　K—N1; 3 Q—B4ch forcing mate.
　　　2 R—R8ch　　KxR
　　　3 QxQ　　Resigns

511　1 RxB!　　QxR
　　　2 N—N5　　. . . .
　　Another way is 2 RxPch, KxR;
　3 N—N5ch and 4 NxQ.
　　　2 . . . .　　Q—N3
　　　3 RxPch　　QxR
　　　4 N—B7 mate

512　1 BxP　　Q—K3
　　　2 B—Q5　　Q—N5
　　If 2 . . . NxB; 3 PxN, Q—N3
　(or 3 . . . Q—B4 or 3 . . . QxP
　with the same result); 4 NxBch
　winning the Queen.
　　　3 QxQ　　NxQ
　　　4 NxBch and wins

513　1 K—N3　　R—Q5
　　If the Rook moves on the file, 2
　NxB wins a piece.
　　　2 N—B5ch　　Resigns
　　White wins the Rook.

514　1 R—Q6　　R—B3
　　Or 1 . . . R—K2; 2 NxNP and
　wins.
　　　2 N—Q7　　. . . .
　　White wins the Exchange.

515　1 R—Q7!　　QxR
　　　2 QxPch　　K—R3
　　　3 Q—N7ch　　K—R4
　　　4 P—N4ch　　K—R5
　　　5 B—Q4　　Resigns
　　White intends 6 B—B2 mate.

516　1 QxRch!　　QxQ
　　　2 R—Q7ch　　QxR
　　　3 RxQch　　. . . .
　　And 4 BxN wins a piece.

517　1 BxNP!　　Q—N4
　　If 1 . . . RxB; 2 Q—B8 mate.
　If 1 . . . QxB; 2 Q—B6 mate.
　　　2 Q—B7!　　P—K4
　　White threatened 3 BxP mate or
　3 QxBP mate.
　　　3 QxRch!　　QxQ
　　　4 B—KR4ch　　Q—N4
　　　5 BxQ mate

518 1 RxN!   QxR
     2 NxBch   PxN
     3 B—B5!   Resigns
Black has no adequate defense
against the coming 4 QxRP and 5
Q—N7 mate.

519 1 RxN!   PxR
     2 RxP   ....
Threatens 3 N—B5 dis ch.
     2 ....   K—B2
     3 N—N5ch   K—B1
     4 R—K6!   ....
Threatens 5 RxNch.
     4 ....   Q—R5
     5 P—N3!   QxRP
     6 R—K8ch!   Resigns
If 6 . . . KxR; 7 Q—K6ch forc-
ing mate.

520 1 QxB!   RxQ
Or 1 . . . QxQ; 2 NxQch, RxN;
3 BxN winning a piece.
     2 N—B6ch   K—R1
     3 NxQ   RxN
     4 BxN and wins

521 1 R—R8ch!   BxR
     2 RxBch   KxR
     3 Q—R6ch   K—N1
     4 N—B6 mate

522 1 N—N6   R—N1
     2 NxB   RxN
     3 BxN   Resigns
White has won a piece.

523 1 ....   R—K6!
If now 2 QxR, Q—R8 mate.
     2 Q—N2   RxP and wins

524 1 ....   RxBch!
     2 QxR   B—Q6ch!
If now 3 K—B1, B—R6 wins.
     3 K—B3   B—N5ch!
     Resigns
If 4 QxB, Q—B7 mate.

525 1 ....   R—N8ch!
If now 2 K—B2, Q—K8 mate.
     2 RxR   QxQ
     Resigns

526 1 ....   B—B7ch!
     Resigns

527 1 ....   BxN
     2 QxB   RxPch!
     3 BxR   QxBch
     4 K—R1   B—K5ch
Black mates next move.

528 1 ....   R—R8ch
     Resigns

529 1 ....   BxN
     2 PxB   P—KN4
Black wins a piece.

530 1 ....   RxPch!
     2 KxR   RxR
Black is two Pawns ahead, and
will soon win a third.

531 1 ....   B—K7!
This wins back the Exchange,
leaving White in a hopeless situation with two Pawns down.

532 1 ....   RxB!
     2 KxR   R—K1ch
After 3 K—Q1 (or 3 K—B1),
BxN Black has a winning game.

533 1 ....   B—R5!
Whichever Bishop White takes,
Black replies 2 . . . QxRch and 3
. . . QxB, with a Rook ahead.

534 1 ....   N—B5
     2 R—B2   NxB
     3 RxN   RxN
     Resigns

535 1 ....   Q—Q3!
Threatening . . . QxQ as well as
the mate that actually occurs. If 2
QxQ, RxR mate.
     2 Q—B3   Q—R7ch
     3 K—B1   Q—R8 mate

536 1 ....   Q—B5!
If now 2 N—B3, QxQ wins a
Rook. If 2 K—B2, RxR; 3 QxR,
QxN etc.
     2 QxQ   RxRch
     3 Q—B1   B—Q5ch
     4 K—R1   RxQ mate

537 1 ....   NxN!
If now 2 NxN, QxRch or 2 KxN,
QxN.
     2 RxQ   BxN
Black comes out a piece ahead.

538 1 ....   N—B7ch
     Resigns
If 2 QxN, QxN mate.

539 1 ....   R—Q8!
     2 QxR   QxKPch
     3 K—N2   N—R5ch!
     4 PxN   B—R6 mate

540
1	RxBch
2 KxR	QxNch
Resigns	

541
1	N—Q5!
2 NxN	....

If the Queen moves, Black wins with . . . NxNch.
2	Q—R7 mate

542
1	BxN
2 QxQ	BxQ
Resigns	

543
1	N—B6ch!
2 K—R1	....

If 2 NxN, QxQ. If 2 PxN, BxNch wins the Queen.
2	NxN
3 QxQch	NxQ
Resigns	

544
1	QxN!
2 BxQ	N—B6ch
3 K—B1	B—N4ch
4 Q—QB4	BxQ mate

545
1	QxPch!
2 NxQ	NxBP mate

546
1	R—N8ch
2 KxR	QxQ
Resigns	

547
1 N—B6!	NxN
2 Q—R7ch!	NxQ
3 B—K5 dbl ch	K—R3
4 B—N7 mate	

548
1 QxR!	PxQ
2 N—B6ch	Resigns

After 3 NxQ White is a Rook ahead.

549
1 RxN!	....

Not 1 BxN allowing . . . RxP with some chances.
1	RxB
2 R—KR8ch!	....

White continues 3 P—Q8/Q.

550
1 NxBP!	KxN
2 N—K4ch	K—N2
3 R—QB2!	Q—R5
4 QxPch	B—N3

Or 4 . . . K—R1; 5 QxR, QxR; 6 QxBch, B—N1; 7 Q—B6 mate.
5 R—B7ch	K—N1

If 5 . . . R—Q2; 6 N—B3 wins.
6 QxBch!	PxQ

551
7 N—B6ch	K—R1
8 R—R7 mate	

551
1 RxPch!	PxR
2 Q—R5 mate	

552
1 B—B6!	QxB
2 KR—K1ch	B—K2

If 2 . . . B—K3; 3 Q—Q7 mate.
3 BxNch	K—B1
4 Q—Q8ch!	BxQ
5 R—K8 mate	

553
1 RxB!	KxR
2 B—K3!	Resigns

If 2 . . . QxB; 3 RxPch, K—Q1; 4 QxN and mate follows.

554
1 B—R6!	BxB
2 N/K4xP	KR—Q1

The threat was 3 Q—R7 mate.
3 R—R8ch!	BxR
4 Q—R7ch	K—B1
5 QxB mate	

555
1 R—K5!	....

Threatens 2 Q—R5ch, K—N1; 3 N—K7ch!, BxN; 4 Q—B7ch and 5 R—R5 mate.
1	R—KB1

If 1 . . . BxR? 2 Q—R5ch, K—N1; 3 N—K7ch and mate next move.
2 N—K7!	Resigns

If 2 . . . RxQ; 3 R—R5 mate.

556
1 P—Q7	Q—Q1

Else the Pawn queens.
2 Q—Q6ch	Resigns

White wins a Rook.

557
1 N—K7ch!	QxN
2 R—R8ch!	KxR

If 2 . . . K—B2; 3 Q—R5ch, P—N3; 4 QxNP mate.
3 Q—R5ch	K—N1
4 Q—R7ch	K—B2
5 B—N6 mate	

558
1 N—N5!	PxN

White threatened 2 Q—R7 mate.
2 Q—K6ch	....

White continues 3 QxR with the Exchange ahead.

559
1 P—K6!	PxP
2 N—K5	Q—K1
3 N—N6ch!	Resigns

If 3 . . . PxN; 4 R—R3ch forces mate.

560 1 P—N6!   QxNP
If 1 . . . QxB; 2 QxP mate. If
1 . . . PxP! 2 N—N5 wins.
    2 BxN!   Resigns
If 2 . . . QxB; 3 R—N1 wins
Black's Queen.

561 1 BxPch!'   KxB
    2 R—R3ch   N—R3
    3 N—B4!   PxN
    4 BxN   PxB
    5 Q—R5   Resigns
Black has no defense.

562 1 N—Q5!   PxN
If 1 . . . Q—B2; 2 Q—R8 mate.
    2 BxQPch   B—K3
    3 BxBch   QxB
    4 RxBch!   KxR
    5 Q—R7ch   K—B3
    6 R—R6 mate

563 1 RxB!   PxR
    2 R—B8!   Q—Q4
If 2 . . . RxR; 3 Q—QR1ch wins;
likewise after 2 . . . QxR; 3 Q—
Q4ch etc.
    3 Q—QR1ch!   P—K4
If 3 . . . RxQ; 4 RxNch forces
mate.
    4 BxPch   QxB
    5 RxNch!   K—N2
    6 R—B7ch!   Resigns
If 6 . . . KxR; 7 NxQch or 6
. . . K—N1, 7 QxRch wins.

564 1 R—K4!   P—N4
    2 R—R4ch!   PxR
    3 Q—R6ch   Resigns
White mates next move.

565 1 R—K8ch!   RxR
    2 Q—N4ch!   QxQ
    3 N—B6 mate

566 1 N—Q5!   KPxN
    2 RxPch!   KxR
    3 QxKNPch   K—B1
    4 R—KB1ch   Resigns
White mates soon.

567 1 N—K7ch!   QxN
    2 QxRPch!   KxQ
    3 R—R5ch   K—N1
    4 R—R8 mate

568 If 1 P—N6, QxNP; 2 Q—
B4ch, P—Q4 and Black has a defense. White therefore uses a clear-

ance move to control the important
diagonal:
    1 N—K5!   PxN
White threatened R—R8 mate.
If 1 . . . QxN; 2 QxQ, PxQ; 3
P—N6 followed by mate.
    2 P—N6!   QxNP
    3 Q—B4ch   Resigns
Interposition at King Bishop 2
allows 4 R—R8 mate.

569 1 P—KB4!   PxP
    2 RxPch!   KxR
    3 Q—R5ch   K—N2
    4 Q—R6ch   K—N1
    5 Q—R8 mate

570 1 P—N5!   BxQNP
    2 N—K6!   P—KR4
White threatened mate in two by
3 Q—B6ch etc.
    3 Q—B6ch   K—R2
    4 B—N4   Resigns
For White plays 5 N—N5ch,
K—R3; 6 B—B8ch followed by
mate.

571 1 N—K5!   Q—K3
Or 1 . . . Q—K1; 2 N/R4—N6ch,
PxN; 3 B—B4!, PxB; 4 R—R1ch,
K—N1; 5 QxPch, R—B2; 6 NxNP
and 7 R—R8 mate.
    2 B—B4!   PxB
    3 P—B5!   QxN
    4 N—N6ch!   PxN
    5 BPxP   QxKNP
    6 R—R1ch   K—N1
    7 QxPch   Q—Q4
    8 R—R8ch!   KxR
    9 Q—R4ch   K—N1
    10 Q—R7 mate

572 1 BxP!   RxB
Or 1 . . . QxB; 2 Q—Q8ch and
mate next move.
    2 Q—R8 mate

573 1 R—R8ch!   KxR
    2 R—R1ch   K—N1
    3 R—R8ch!   KxR
    4 Q—R1ch   K—N1
    5 Q—R7 mate

574 1 Q—Q8ch   Q—B1
    2 RxPch!   BxR
    3 Q—B6ch   Q—N2
If 3 . . . B—N2; 4 R—R1 mate.
    4 R—R1!   QxQ
    5 PxQ   . . . .
White mates next move.

575   1 BxP!   P—K3

575	1 BxP!	P—K3
	If 1 . . . NxQ; 2 BxP mate.	
	2 B—N5ch	K—K2
	If 2 . . . N—Q2; 3 BxNch, QxB;	
	4 Q—B4 with a piece ahead.	
	3 N—N6ch!	RPxN
	4 N—Q5ch!	PxN
	5 Q—K5 mate	

576	1 B—N5!	QxQB
	2 Q—KB5ch!	QxQ
	3 RxRch	KxR
	4 R—K8 mate	
	(Another way is 1 RxRch, KxR;	
	2 B—N5ch etc.)	

577	1	N—K7ch
	2 K—R1	QxN!
	3 PxQ	R—R4ch!
	4 PxR	R—R5 mate

578	1	K—N2
	Threatens 2 . . . R—R1ch and	
	3 . . . Q—R6 (or 3 . . . R—R8ch!).	
	2 P—K6	R—R1ch
	3 K—N1	Q—K1
	4 P—KN4	R—R8ch!
	5 KxR	Q—R1ch
	6 K—N1	Q—R6
	And Black checkmates.	

579	1	QxR
	2 RxQ	N—Q6ch
	After 3 . . . NxQ Black will be	
	a Rook ahead.	

580	1	Q—N1!
	2 PxP	B—R6!
	3 PxPch	K—Q2!
	4 QxB	R—R1ch
	5 K—N1	R—R8ch!
	6 KxR	R—R1ch
	7 K—N1	R—R8ch!
	8 KxR	Q—KR1ch
	9 K—N1	Q—R7ch
	10 KxN	Q—R8 mate

581	1	P—K6!
	2 PxP	PxP
	3 NxP	N—Q6ch!
	4 PxN	QxPch
	5 K—K2	N—Q5 mate

582	1	B—N4!
	2 PxB	N/R4—N6ch!
	3 NxN	NxNch
	4 PxN	PxP dis ch
	5 K—N1	R—R8ch!
	6 KxR	R—R1ch

	7 K—N1	B—B4ch!
	8 NxB	R—R8ch!
	9 KxR	Q—R1ch
	10 K—N1	Q—R7 mate

583	1 R—Q5!	Resigns
	If 1 . . . PxR; 2 QxRch and mate	
	next move. If 1 . . . QxR; 2 Q—B6	
	mate.	

584	1 B—Q6!	Resigns
	If 1 . . . QxQ; 2 R—B8 mate. If	
	1 . . . RxB; 2 Q—N8ch and mate	
	follows.	

585	1 B—K6ch!	K—N1
	If 1 . . . PxB; 2 Q—Q7ch forces	
	mate.	
	2 N—Q7ch	K—B1
	3 N—B5 dis ch	K—N1
	4 N—R6ch!	PxN
	5 Q—N4 mate	

586	1 B—K4!	BxB
	If 1 . . . RxB; 2 P—R3ch, K—	
	N6; 3 R—B3 mate.	
	3 P—R3ch	K—N6
	3 B—K1 mate	

587	1 R—B5!	PxR
	2 QxP mate	

588	1 R—Q7!	BxR
	2 BxPch!	NxB
	If 2 . . . K—R1; 3 NxP mate.	
	3 QxPch	K—R1
	4 N—N6 mate	

589	1 N—K4!	BxN
	2 RxB	Resigns
	If 2 . . . PxR; 3 Q—N3 mate.	

590	1 P—K7!	NxP
	2 BxN	RxB
	3 QxNPch	K—B1
	4 RxPch	Resigns
	White wins after 4 . . . K—K1;	
	5 Q—N8ch, K—Q2; 6 B—B5ch	
	etc.	

591	1 N—K6ch!	PxN
	2 Q—B8ch	K—B2
	3 QxNch	K—N1
	4 R—R8ch	B—B1
	5 RxBch	KxR
	6 B—R6ch	. . . .
	White mates next move.	

592	1 R—KN3ch	K—B2
	2 QxQch	Resigns

593
  1 B—Q6!   BxB
  2 N—B6ch!   PxN
  3 R—N1ch   K—R1
  4 QxPch!   KxQ
  5 R—KR5 mate

594
  1 B—B7!   QxB
If 1 . . . RxB; 2 Q—N7ch!, RxQ;
3 RxP mate.
  2 RxPch!   QxR
  3 Q—N7ch   KxP
  4 R—R1 mate

595
  1 P—K7!   R—B2
If 1 . . . QxP; 2 QxQPch, K—R1;
3 KxB and wins.
If 1 . . . R—B3; 2 P—K8/Qch
winning.
If 1 . . . KR—K1; 2 RxPch!,
KxR; 3 R—N1ch forcing mate.
  2 RxPch!   KxR
If 2 . . . RxR; 3 P—K8/Qch
wins.
  3 R—N1ch   ....
White forces mate.

596
  1 R—QB7!   N—K3
White threatened 2 Q—N7 mate.
  2 RxB and wins

597
  1 N—B8!   RxN
If 1 . . . QxQ; 2 R—N8 mate.
If 1 . . . QxN; 2 R—N8ch, QxR;
3 Q—KB6ch and mate follows.
  2 R—N8ch!   RxR
  3 QxQch   R—N2
  4 QxR mate

598
  1 QxPch!   PxQ
  2 P—B7ch!   QxP
  3 R—R8 mate

599
  1 RxN   Q—R5
  2 R—B2   RxN
  3 R—K7!   Resigns
There is no good defense to the
coming 4 QxBch.

600
  1 N—K6!   Resigns
Black is helpless against 2 QxB
mate.

601
  1 P—R6!   B—B3
  2 PxP   PxP
  3 QxP and wins

602
  1 N—B5!   ....
Threatens 2 QxP mate.
  1 ....   BxN
  2 Q—B6ch   K—N1

  3 QxRch   B—N3
  4 Q—B6   Resigns
White forces mate.

603
  1 R—K3!   Resigns
If 1 . . . BxR; 2 QxNP mate.

604
  1 Q—K6!!   BxQ
If 1 . . . RxQ; 2 N/R4—N6 dis
ch, K—N1; 3 R—R8 mate.
If 1 . . . NxN; 2 N/R4—N6 dis
ch also leads to mate.
  2 N—B5 dis ch K—N1
  3 N—K7 mate

605
  1 R—Q6!   BxR
  2 QxPch   K—R1
Or 2 . . . K—B1; 3 QxR/B5ch
etc.
  3 QxR/K8ch   R—B1
  4 BxPch!   Resigns
If 4 . . . BxB; 5 QxRch etc.

606 If 1 P—B6, apparently winning, Black has the resource 1 . . .
Q—B4ch. White blocks off this defense by:
  1 R—K5!   BxR
If 1 . . . PxN; 2 Q—N7 mate.
  2 P—B6   Resigns
If 2 . . . BxP; 3 QxBch and
mate next move.

607
  1 ....   R—N8!
  2 KxR   P—B7
  Resigns
White cannot stop the Pawn
from queening.

608
  1 ....   B—K6!
If now 2 BxB, P—R6! 3 P—N3,
Q—B6 forcing mate. If 2 PxB,
QxKNP mate.
  2 QxB   RxQ
  3 PxR   P—R6
  4 R—B2   Q—Q8ch
  5 R—B1   P—R7ch
  Resigns

609
  1 ....   P—KN4!
Threatens . . . Q—R5 mate.
  2 PxP e. p.   BxB
Black wins easily, as White's
threat is gone.

610
  1 ....   B—Q3!
  2 RxB   ....
If 2 BxB, P—Q8/Q.
  2 ....   P—R7
And Black wins, as one of his
Pawns must queen.

611 1 ....   R—K6!
 If now 2 QxR, QxRch and mate
next move.
         2 PxR   Q—K7
         3 QxP   ....
 If 3 R—Q2, Q—B8 mate.
         3 ....   QxRch
         4 K—B2   Q—B8 mate

612 1 ....   B—Q6ch!
         2 QxB   ....
 If 2 K—N2?, QxN mate.
         2 ....   QxRch
 Black has won the Exchange.

613 Unable to play . . . QxR or
. . . PxR, Black nevertheless finds a
clever interference device:
         1 ....   N—K7ch!
         2 BxN   ....
 If 2 RxN, QxR.
         2 ....   QxPch
 Followed by 3 . . . PxR and
Black has won the Exchange.

614 1 ....   N—B5!
 Threatens . . . N—K7ch winning
the Queen.
         2 PxN   QxR and wins

615 1 ....   R—Q6!
         2 QxR   ....
 If 2 BxR, QxPch; 3 K—N1,
Q—N7 mate.
         2 ....   NxQ
         3 BxN   Q—Q3ch
 Followed by 4 . . . QxB with an
easy win.

616 1 ....   P—B7ch!
 If now 2 RxP, BxP!; 3 PxR,
R—R8 mate.
         2 QxP   RxP!
         3 QxR   BxP
         4 Q—K2   ....
 If 4 Q—R3, QxPch; 5 K—B1,
RxB! wins.
         4 ....   B—B5 dis ch
         5 K—B1   BxP
         6 Q—R2   ....
 If 6 K—K1, Q—N6ch wins.
         6 ....   BxN and wins
 The double pin cripples White.

617 1 ....   N—B6ch!
         2 PxN   QxRch
 Black has won the Exchange and
will queen his passed Pawn.

618 1 ....   R—N6!
 If now 2 PxR, Q—K6ch and
mate next move.
         2 QxR   B—R5!
         3 QxB   Q—K6ch
 Black mates next move.

619 1 ....   R—B6!
         2 PxR   BxPch
 Followed by . . . BxR and Black
is a Pawn ahead.

620 1 ....   P—QB4!
 If now 2 N—N3 or N—B2, Black
plays 2 . . . NxPch and 3 . . . BxN
winning the Exchange.
         2 N/Q4—K2   NxQBP
 Black has won a Pawn.

621 White, who is ahead in material, expects 1 . . . K—B1 when
he wins with 2 R—B4ch!, for if 2
. . . PxR; 3 Q—N7 mate. But
Black has a beautiful blocking
move:
         1 ....   Q—B2!
         2 BxQch   K—B1!
         Resigns
 White cannot stop . . . R—KR8
mate!

622 1 ....   Q—Q3ch
         2 K—R3   N—B5ch
         3 K—N3   N—R4 dbl ch
         4 K—R3   Q—N6ch!
         5 RxQ   N—B5 mate

623 1 ....   P—Q5!
         2 QxQP   QxNP mate

624 1 ....   R—B7!
 If now 2 QxR, RxRch and mate
next move.
         2 Q—R5   B—B6!
         3 RxR   QxR
         4 Q—Q8ch   K—N2
         5 R—KN1   B—Q5
         6 B—Q6   QxNPch!
         7 RxQ   R—B8ch
         8 R—N1   RxR mate

625 1 B—B4ch!   ....
 Not 1 B—N5?, K—B2.
         1 ....   K—R1
 If 1 . . . NxB? the Pawn queens.
         2 B—N5!   Resigns
 2 B—B7! also wins.

230 · SOLUTIONS ·

626
1 QxPch!	PxQ
2 P—N7ch	K—R2
3 PxR/Nch	K—R1
4 R—N8 mate	

627
1 N—K3!	N—Q3

If 1 . . . NxN; 2 R—B8ch wins.
2 R—B8ch	Resigns

If 2 . . . N/Q3xR; 3 RxR! wins.

628
1 P—B4!	R—K6
2 P—B5!	R—K4
3 R—Q8!	B—R4
4 P—B6!	BxR

If 4 . . . PxP; 5 BxP mate.
5 P—B7!	Resigns

Black cannot prevent the Pawn
from queening.

629 White cannot win by 1 NxB be-
cause of 1 . . . R—N8ch!; 2 RxR,
QxRch; 3 K—B2, Q—B7ch; 4 K—
N3, Q—N3ch.
1 QxR!	PxQ
2 NxB	Resigns

Black is helpless against P—R7
and P—R8/Qch.

630
1 QxR!	QxQ
2 P—Q7 dis ch Resigns	

White continues 3 P—Q8/Q.

631
1 P—K8/Qch!	KxQ
2 B—R4	Resigns

632
1 P—B5ch!	PxP
2 PxPch	K—Q3

Forced. Now White can win with
3 B—Q2, but he chooses an even
prettier way:
3 RxB!	RxR
4 B—B5ch!	Resigns

If 4 . . . KxB; 5 P—B7 wins.

633
1 R—Q8ch!	RxR
2 R—B8ch!	KxR
3 PxR/Qch	Resigns

634
1 RxN!	RxR
2 P—K7	R—N1
3 R—Q8	Resigns

There follows 4 RxRch, KxR;
5 P—K8/Qch.

635
1 Q—N5!	QxQ
2 P—B8/Qch	K—B2
3 QxNch!	KxQ
4 N—B7ch and wins	

White continues 5 NxQ.

636
1 R—Q6ch!	RxR
2 P—N8/Q	Resigns

637
1 Q—K6ch!	QxQ
2 PxQ	Resigns

Black cannot stop the Pawn.

638
1 QxRch!	NxQ
2 P—Q7	Resigns

White's twofold threat of 3 Px
Nch or 3 P—Q8ch is decisive.

639
1 N—R5!	PxP

If 1 . . . NxN; 2 PxP wins.
2 NxN	KxN
3 P—R7	K—N2
4 P—B5!	Resigns

Black is helpless against the
Pawns.

640
1 R—B8ch!	K—R2

If 1 . . . KxR; 2 R—B1ch, K—
N1; 3 P—K7 dis ch wins.
2 P—K7!	QxP
3 RxR	Resigns

If 3 . . . QxR; 4 N—B6ch! wins
the Queen.

641
1 QxRch!	QxQ
2 P—B7	Resigns

Black is helpless.

642
1 QxR!	PxQ
2 P—R6	Resigns

The Pawn marches in.

643
1 RxB!	RxR
2 RxR	KxR

If 2 . . . QxR; 3 Q—Q8 mate.
3 Q—Q7ch!	QxQ
4 PxQ	Resigns

White queens the Pawn.

644
1 R—B8!	RxR
2 R—K8ch!	NxR
3 P—Q7!	N—Q3
4 PxQR/Q	NxQ
5 PxP!	Resigns

The Pawn must queen!

645
1 Q—R8ch!	KxQ
2 P—N7ch	K—N1
3 B—R7ch!	KxB
4 P—N8/Q mate	

646
1 R—B8ch!	RxR
2 QxPch!	KxQ
3 PxR/Nch!	Resigns

White wins easily after 4 NxQ.

647
1 P—R8/Qch	RxQ
2 N—B5ch	K—N1
3 RxRch	KxR
4 Q—R6ch	K—N1
5 Q—N7 mate	

648
1 RxN!	KxR

Forced.
2 N—B5ch	K—K1

If 2 . . . K—B2; 3 N—K6ch wins the Rook; likewise after 3 . . . K—Q3; 4 N—N7ch.
3 N—K6!	R—Q8ch

If 3 . . . R—R1; 4 N—B7ch wins.
4 K—R2	R—QR8
5 P—R8/Qch	RxQ
6 N—B7ch	Resigns

White wins the Rook.

649
1	P—K5ch!
2 BxP	NxB
3 KxN	P—B7

The Pawn queens.

650
1	QxP!
2 RxQ	PxR
Resigns	

White cannot stop the Pawn from queening.

651
1	RxP!
2 NxR	Q—B8ch
3 K—R2	P—N8/Q mate

652
1	QxRch!
2 QxQ	R—K8ch
Resigns	

653
1	RxP!

If now 2 RxR, P—N8/Q.
2 R—QN1	K—B6
Resigns	

Black wins a Rook with 3 . . . K—B7 etc.

654
1	Q—K2!
2 PxQ	B—N2
Resigns	

After 3 QxP, BxQ Black will win the Rook, remaining the Exchange and several Pawns ahead.

655
1	QxR!
2 QxQ	P—R8/Q
Resigns	

Black has won a Rook.

656
1	PxB!
2 RxB	QxR

3 R—B1	Q—B7!
Resigns	

If 4 RxQ, QPxR followed by 5 . . . R—Q8 and wins.

657 White threatens R—KN8 mate. If Black tries 1 . . . RxN? then 2 R—QN8ch leads to mate. But Black underpromotes to win:
1	P—B8/Nch!
2 K—N1	N—N6 dis ch
3 RxR	RxRch
4 K—R2	N—B8ch
5 K—R1	N—K6 dis ch
6 R—N1	RxRch
7 KxR	NxP
Resigns	

658
1	R—R6ch
2 K—B2	RxB
3 PxR	P—R6
Resigns	

The Pawn must queen.

659
1	N—N6ch!
2 PxN	PxP dis ch
3 K—N1	N—B7

Threatens mate.
4 RxN	R—R8ch!
5 KxR	PxR
Resigns	

The Pawn queens.

660
1	R—K8!
2 RxR	NxR
Resigns	

The Pawn must queen.

661
1	P—Q7!
Resigns	

If 2 QxQ, PxR/Q mate. If 2 R—Q1, QxQ wins.

662 White has just played QxQ. Instead of replying . . . NxQ, Black nonchalantly advances to queen:
1	P—N7!
2 Q—B3	B—N5!
3 QxB	NxQ
Resigns	

The Pawn must queen.

663
1	B—N7!
Resigns	

Black will come out a piece ahead.

664
1	QxPch!
2 KxQ	R—R5ch
3 K—N1	R—R8ch!
4 NxR	PxN/Q mate

665 1 ....   BxP!
    2 NxB   P—N6
    3 N—B3   ....
If 3 N—B1, P—N7 wins.
    3 ....   P—N7
Followed by 4 . . . P—R7 and
Black queens a Pawn.

666 1 ....   RxNch!
    2 KxR   P—K7
    3 R—B1   PxR/Qch
    4 KxQ   NxB
    Resigns

667 1 R—B8!   RxR
If 1 . . . QxQP; 2 Q—B8ch!
forces mate.
    2 Q—K7!   P—R3
If 2 . . . QxQ; 3 PxR/Qch and
mate next move.
    3 QxQ   PxQ
    4 PxR/Qch   Resigns

668 1 RxR   QxR
    2 Q—R4!   Resigns
Black loses his Rook, as he can-
not go in for 2 . . . QxQ; 3 R—
N8ch forcing mate.

669 1 QxN!   PxQ
    2 RxRch   B—K1
    3 BxP!   QxB
    4 RxB mate

670 1 B—K6!   PxB
If 1 . . . RxR; 2 Q—K8 mate.
If 1 . . . BxB; 2 Q—B8ch or Q—
R8ch leads to mate.
    2 Q—B8ch   ....
2 Q—R8ch leads to the same re-
sult.
    2 ....   B—Q1
    3 QxBch!   ....
White forces mate.

671 1 QxRch!   KxQ
    2 R—K8 mate

672 1 QxP!   RxQ
    2 R—B8ch!   BxR
    3 R—K8ch   R—B1
    4 RxR mate

673 1 Q—B4ch   K—R1
Or 1 . . . R—B2; 2 P—Q7, Q—
Q7; 3 QR—Q1 and wins.
    2 QxN!   Resigns
If 2 . . . PxQ; 3 RxR mate.

674 1 Q—N3ch   ....
Or 1 Q—B4ch with the same
effect.
    1 ....   K—R1
    2 Q—B7!   Resigns
If 2 . . . RxR; 3 QxR mate. If
2 . . . RxQ; 3 RxRch leads to
mate. Meanwhile White threatens
3 QxP mate.

675 1 Q—B3!   Q—B4
If 1 . . . QxQ; 2 RxR mate.
    2 RxRch   QxR
    3 QxR   Resigns

676 1 RxP!   NxR
Or 1 . . . QxQ; 2 R—K8 mate.
    2 Q—B8ch   ....
White mates next move.

677 1 N—B5!   R—Q2
If 1 . . . PxN; 2 R—Q8ch leads
to mate.
    2 BxR and wins

678 1 QxNch!   RxQ
    2 R—Q8ch   R—B1
    3 RxR mate

679 1 Q—B7!   Q—N4
If 1 . . . QxQ or . . . RxQ; 2
RxRch forces mate.
    2 P—QR4!   QxRP
    3 R—K4!   Q—N4
If 3 . . . QxR; 4 RxQ wins. If
3 . . . RxR; 4 QxRch forces mate.
If 3 . . . RxQ; 4 RxRch forces
mate.
    4 QxNP!   Resigns
If 4 . . . QxQ; 5 RxRch and
mate next move. Black has no good
move.

680 1 QxB!   PxQ
    2 N—B7ch   K—N1
If 2 . . . RxN; 3 R—K8ch forcing mate.
    3 NxQ and wins

681 1 RxPch!   NxR
    2 Q—KB7ch   K—R1
    3 Q—B8ch!   RxQ
    4 RxR mate

682 1 RxNch!   KxR
    2 QxRch!   Resigns
If 2 . . . PxQ; 3 R—B8ch and
mate in two more moves.

683 1 N—R6ch   K—R1
      2 QxB!   QxQ
      3 NxPch!   K—N1
If 3 . . . RxN; 4 R—Q8ch leads
to mate.
      4 NxQ and wins

684 1 QxR!   RxQ
      2 R—Q8ch   RxR
      3 RxR mate

685 1 ....   P—QN4!
      2 QxBP   ....
No matter where the Queen
plays, White can no longer prevent
Black's next move.
      2 ....   Q—B8ch!
      3 RxQ   RxR mate

686 1 ....   P—B6ch!
      2 K—N1   QxRch!
      3 KxQ   R—Q8 mate

687 1 ....   B—R3!
If now 2 BxB, Q—KB7ch; 3
K—R1, Q—B8ch forcing mate.
      2 R—K1   BxBch
      3 QxB   R—B8ch!
      4 RxR   QxQch and wins

688 1 ....   RxP!
If now 2 QxQ, RxRch with mate
to follow.
      2 RxR   RxR!
For if 3 QxR, Q—K8 mate.
      3 Q—Q1   QxP and wins

689 1 ....   R—B8!
      2 RxR   Q—Q8ch!
      3 RxQ   RxR mate

690 1 ....   QxRch!
      2 NxR   N—B6ch!
      3 QxN   R—K8ch
      4 B—B1   RxB mate

691 1 ....   B—KB4!
If now 2 QxB, QxQ; 3 NxQ,
NxBch and mate follows.
      2 NxB   QxN!
      3 QxQ   NxBch
      4 K—R1   R—B8ch
      5 Q—N1   RxQ mate

692 1 ....   BxP!
If now 2 QxB or RxB, then 2
. . . Q—B8ch leads to mate.
      2 Q—N3   Q—B8ch
      3 RxQ   RxR mate

693 1 ....   R—B4!
      2 RxR   ....
If 2 RxQ, R—B8 mate. If 2
PxR, Q—Q8 mate.
      2 ....   QxQ and wins

694 1 ....   QxNch!
      2 RxQ   R—N8ch
      3 Q—Q1   RxQch
      4 R—B1   B—Q5ch
      5 K—R1   RxR mate

695 1 ....   Q—N7!
If now 2 QxQ, R—Q8 mate. If 2
Q—Q3, Q—R8ch! wins.
      2 R—Q3   Q—N8ch!
      Resigns

696 1 ....   NxP!
If now 2 PxN, QxPch; 3 K—R1,
R—Q8ch! forces mate; while if 3
K—B1, R—Q7; 4 Q—QB5, R—
B7ch; 5 K—N1, RxB dis ch wins.
      2 R—K4   QxR!
So that if 3 BxQ, R—Q8ch forces
mate.
      3 Q—K2   QxB!
      Resigns
If 4 PxQ, R—Q8ch; 5 RxR, Rx
Rch; 6 QxR, NxQ leaving Black a
piece ahead.

697 1 ....   Q—Q3!
Attacking Rook and Knight.
      2 RxQ   R—K8ch
      3 K—R2   R—KR8 mate

698 White hopes for 1 . . . RxQ?;
2 NxRch, K moves; 3 NxQ winning the King and Pawn ending.
      1 ....   QxN!
      Resigns
If 2 QxR, Q—K8 mate. If 2 PxQ,
R—Q8ch and mate next move.

699 1 ....   Q—K5!
      Resigns
If 2 QxQ, RxRch followed by
mate. If 2 Q—K2, QxQ; 3 RxQ,
RxRch and mate follows.

700 1 ....   N—K5!
      Resigns
If 2 QxQ, RxR mate. Or 2 PxN,
RxR mate.

701 1 ....   Q—Q7!
      Resigns
If 2 QxQ, R—B8 mate. On other

Queen moves Black can play . . . QxR.

702
1 ....　　　　N—N5!
2 QxQ　　　　R—B8 mate

703
1 Q—R6!　　　PxQ
2 NxP mate

704
1 QxPch!　　　BxQ
2 R—B7ch　　K—Q3
3 N—N5ch　　K—Q4
4 P—B4ch　　K—K5
5 R—K1 mate

705
1 QxNch!　　　PxQ
Or 1 . . . K—N1; 2 N—Q7ch
winning.
2 B—R6ch　　K—N1
3 NxP mate

706
1 B—R6!　　　Resigns
If 1 . . . QxQ or . . . RxQ; 2
R—B8 mate.

707
1 B—R7!　　　KxB
2 Q—N6ch!　　PxQ
If 2 . . . K—R1; 3 QxRP mate.
3 PxPch　　　K—R1
4 RxP mate

708
1 Q—R6ch!　　KxQ
2 N/R4—B5ch　BxN
3 NxBch　　　K—R4
4 P—KN4ch　　KxP
5 R—N3ch　　K—R4
6 B—K2 mate

709
1 R—Q7!　　　QR—Q1
2 RxB!　　　　RxR
3 Q—B6!　　　Resigns
If 3 . . . PxQ; 4 R—N4ch, K—
R1; 5 BxP mate.

710
1 QxN!　　　　BxQ
2 RxP!　　　　PxR
3 RxP　　　　....
White forces mate.

711
1 QxNPch!　　KxQ
2 KR—N1ch　　K—B1
3 BxN　　　　Q—R6
4 R—N8ch!　　KxR
5 RxQ　　　　....
Followed by 6 R—R8 mate.

712
1 Q—R7ch!　　K—B1
If 1 . . . NxQ; 2 PxNch, K—R1;
3 R—B8 mate.

2 Q—R8ch　　K—K2
3 QxPch　　　Resigns
White wins the Queen.

713
1 Q—R6ch!　　K—K2
If 1 . . . RxQ; 2 BxRch, K—K2;
3 N—N8 mate!
2 N—N8ch!　　RxN
2 B—N5ch　　P—B3
4 PxPch　　　K—B2
5 Q—R7ch　　K—B1
6 B—R6ch　　....
And White mates.

714
1 R—KN5!　　RxQ
If 1 . . . P—N3; 2 N—R6 mate.
If 1 . . . N—N3; 2 QxRch, RxQ;
3 RxRch, B—B1; 4 P—R5, N—R1;
5 RxP mate.
2 N—R6ch　　K—R1
3 BxP mate

715
1 QxNch!　　　PxQ
2 B—QR6 mate

716
1 N—B7ch!　　QxN
If 1 . . . K—B1; 2 P—K6, QxN;
3 P—K7ch and wins.
2 BxPch　　　K—Q2
3 Q—B5ch!　　NxQ
4 P—K6 mate

717
1 QxRPch!　　KxQ
2 R—R4ch　　K—N1
3 R—K8 mate

718
1 Q—K8ch!　　KxQ
2 N—B6ch　　K—Q1
3 N—B7 mate

719
1 QxB!　　　　RxQ
Or 1 . . . QxR; 2 Q—N7 mate.
2 RxQch　　　PxR
3 RxR and wins
White is a Rook ahead.

720
1 QxKPch!　　PxQ
2 R—K6 mate

721
1 QxN!　　　　PxQ
2 R—B3　　　....
Followed by 3 R—R3 mate.

722
1 B—N7ch　　K—B2
2 Q—K6ch!　　NxQ
3 PxN mate

723
1 Q—N6ch!　　K—K2
If 1 . . . PxQ; 2 B—N4 mate.
2 P—Q6ch　　K—B1
Other moves are even worse.

3 PxP and wins
Black has no good defense.

724 1 P—B5ch!   PxP
Or 1 . . . KxP; 2 Q—B3ch and
White wins as in the main line.
    2 QxPch!   K—N2
If 2 . . . KxQ; 3 N—B4 mate.
    3 P—N6   Resigns
Black is helpless against the com-
ing Q—R7ch and Q—B7 mate.

725 1 QxNch!   QxQ
    2 RxP mate

726 1 QxNch!   PxQ
    2 B—B6 mate

727 1 QxRPch!   KxQ
    2 R—R3ch   K—N1
    3 R—R8 mate

728 1 QxN!   NxQ
    2 RxRch   K—N2
    3 N—N4   QxP
    4 B—B3ch   P—B3
    5 BxPch   K—B2
    6 R—KR8   Q—N5
Or 6 . . . P—K4; 7 RxPch with
a mating attack.
    7 RxPch   K—N1
    8 R—Q8ch   KxR
    9 R—R8 mate

729 1 Q—Q5!   P—K3
White threatened 2 QxBP mate.
    2 QxKP!   PxQ
    3 BxPch   Q—B2
    4 RxB!   QxB
    5 R—B8 mate

730 1 QxB!   QxQ
    2 N—Q7ch   K—R1
    3 N—QB6 dis ch N—R3
    4 N—N6 mate

731 1 Q—N5ch!   PxQ
    2 BxP mate
(White has a less showy mate
with 1 B—KN5ch, etc.)

732 1 QxP!   PxQ
If 1 . . . Q—K1; 2 Q—R5, N—
K3; 3 KR—B1 White wins quickly.
    2 RxPch   K—N1
    3 RxP dis ch   K—B1
    4 RxQ and wins
White is a Pawn ahead, and
threatens to win a piece with 5
BxN.

733 1 Q—N5!   P—N3
If 1 . . . QxQ; 2 RxR mate.
    2 Q—R6!   PxN
    3 R—N4ch!   PxR
    4 BxPch   K—R1
    5 B—N6 dis ch K—N1
    6 Q—R7ch   K—B1
    7 QxP mate

734 1 N/B4—K5!   NxN
    2 NxN!   BxQ
    3 BxPch   N—Q2
If 3 . . . K—Q1; 4 RxBch, K—
B1; 5 B—R6ch, K—N1; 6 N—
B6ch, QxN; 7 B—K5ch, Q—Q3;
8 R—B1! forcing mate.
    4 BxNch   QxB
If 4 . . . K—Q1; 5 RxB and
Black is helpless.
    5 NxQ and wins
White has won a Pawn!

735 1 QxPch!   KxQ
    2 PxB dis ch   K—N3
    3 RxBch   K—N3
    4 N—K7 mate

736 1 Q—B7ch!   RxQ
    2 PxR mate

737 1 QxRPch!   KxQ
    2 R—R1ch   B—R6
    3 RxB mate

738 1 Q—R6ch!   KxQ
If 1 . . . K—R1; 2 QxRPch!,
KxQ; 3 PxP dbl ch, K—N2; 4
R—R7 mate.
    2 PxP dis ch   K—N4
    3 R—R5ch!   KxR
    4 P—B4 dis ch   NxB
    5 N—B6ch   K—R3
    6 R—R1ch   K—N2
    7 N—K8ch!   RxN
    8 RxPch   K—B3
    9 RxP mate

739 1 QxNPch!   NxQ
    2 RxNch   K—R1
    3 R—N8 dbl ch! KxR
    4 R—KN1ch   Q—N4
    5 RxQ mate

740 1 Q—N6!   BPxQ
If 1 . . . RPxQ; 2 R—R3 mate.
If 1 . . . R—N1; 2 QxRPch, KxQ;
3 R—R3 mate.
    2 N/K7xPch   PxN
    3 R—R3 mate

741	1 QxNch!	KxQ
	2 R—Q1ch	K—B1
	3 R—B8ch	Q—K1
	4 RxQch	B—Q1
	5 RxB mate	
742	1 Q—N6ch!	BxQ
	2 N—N5ch!	PxN
	3 PxB mate	
743	1 QxPch!	KxQ
	2 NxB dbl ch	K—R3

If 2 . . . K—R1; 3 N—N6 mate.

	3 N/K5—N4ch	K—N4
	4 P—KR4ch	K—B5
	5 P—KN3ch	K—B6
	6 B—K2ch	K—N7
	7 R—R2ch	K—N8
	8 K—Q2 mate	
744	1 R—R8ch	K—B2
	2 QxNch!	KxQ
	3 R/R1—R7 mate	
745	1	QxR!
	2 PxQ	B—B4ch
	3 Q—B2	R—R8ch!
	4 KxR	BxQ

No matter what White does, there follows . . . R—QR1 mate.

746	1	Q—R8ch!
	2 KxQ	B—B6ch
	3 K—N1	R—Q8 mate
747	1	BxP!

If now 2 NxQ, N—Q5 mate!

	2 B—N2	N—N5 dis ch
	3 K—B1	QxN! and wins

Black wins a piece because of the threat of . . . N—Q6ch.

748	1	QxN!
	2 BxQ	RxRch
	3 K—B2	N—N5ch
	4 K—B3	NxRPch
	5 K—B2	R—KB8 mate
749	1	QxPch!
	2 KxQ	N—N5ch
	3 K—N1	N—R6ch
	4 K—B1	N—R7 mate
750	1	QxB!
	2 PxQ	R—N3ch
	3 K—R1	B—R6

If now 4 R—N1, RxRch; 5 KxR, R—K8ch and mate next move. Or 4 Q—Q3, P—KB4!; 5 Q—QB4ch, K—B1! and wins.

	4 R—Q1	B—N7ch
	5 K—N1	B/N7xP dis ch
	6 K—B1	R—N7!

If now 7 QxB, RxRP leads to mate; or 7 Q—K2, RxQ; 8 P—Q4, RxRP forcing mate.

	7 Q—Q3	RxBPch
	8 K—N1	R—N7 dbl ch
	9 K moves	R—N8 mate
751	1	Q—R6!
	2 PxQ	NxP mate
752	1	Q—R5ch!
	2 KxQ	B—B7ch
	4 K—N5	P—R3 mate
753	1	Q—B8!
	2 RxQ	RxR mate
754	1	RxB!
	2 NxR	QxRch!
	3 QxQ	BxNch

If now 4 K—B1, B—B5ch; 5 B—K2, NxP mate.

	4 K—R1	N—B7ch
	Resigns	

For after 5 K—N1, N—Q6 dis ch and 6 . . . NxQ Black remains a piece ahead.

755	1	N—N5!
	Resigns	

Black threatens . . . QxP mate. If 2 QxQ, N—B7 mate.

756	1	Q—KN6!

Threatens 2 . . . QxRP mate.

	2 QxQ	. . . .

If 2 RPxQ, N—K7 mate. If 2 BPxQ, N—K7ch; 3 K—R1, RxR mate.

	2	N—K7ch
	3 K—R1	NxQch
	4 K—N1	N—K7ch

Black is a piece ahead.

757	1 R—R8!	RxP
	2 R—R7ch	. . . .

White wins the Rook.
(1 R—KN8 also wins.)

758	1 R—R8ch!	K—B2

If 1 . . . KxR; 2 Q—R6ch and mate next move.

	2 RxR	QxN
	3 RxPch	Resigns

There might follow 3 . . . N—Q2; 4 QxQch, KxQ; 5 RxN etc.

759
```
1 RxN!          PxR
2 R—Q1ch        ....
```
White wins the Queen.

760
```
1 Q—N6ch        K—K2
2 RxNch!        QxR
3 Q—N7ch        K—Q3
```
Other King moves lose the Queen
or run into mate.
```
4 B—B4ch        Resigns
```

761
```
1 B—QR3         N—B3
2 N—K7ch!       QxN
3 BxN and wins
```

762
```
1 R—QR1ch       K—N1
2 R—R8ch        K—B2
3 R—R7ch        ....
```
White wins the Rook.

763
```
1 Q—R7ch        Q—K2
2 B—B8!         QxQ
3 RxQch         ....
```
White will be a piece ahead.

764
```
1 N—K5ch        K—K3
2 Q—KN8ch       Resigns
```
White wins the Queen.

765
```
1 QR—QB1!  N/B4—Q2
```
If 1 . . . N/N1—Q2; 2 NxN,
NxN; 3 R—B8ch winning a Rook;
or 2 . . . KxN; 3 RxN winning a
piece.
```
2 R—B8ch        K—B2
3 RxR and wins
```
White has won the Exchange.

766
```
1 Q—N8ch        K—Q3
2 B—R3ch        K—B3
3 Q—QR8ch       Resigns
```
White wins the Queen.

767
```
1 QxRch!        KxQ
```
Or 1 . . . QxQ; 2 RxB and
White will be a Rook ahead.
```
2 RxBch         K—B2
3 R—B8ch        K—N3
4 RxQ and wins
```

768
```
1 P—B5!         ....
```
Threatens 2 P—QR3, B—R4; 3
P—QN4 winning a piece.
```
1 ....          PxP
2 P—QR3         B—R4
3 PxP           ....
```
If now 3 . . . QxP; 4 P—QN4
wins a piece.
```
3 ....          P—B3
4 B—Q6 and wins
```
White wins the Exchange.

769
```
1 RxPch!        KxR
2 Q—K7ch        K—N3
```
If 2 . . . K—R3; 3 R—KR8ch.
```
3 R—KN8ch       K—B4
4 RxNch!        KxR
```
If 4 . . . PxR; 5 Q—Q7ch.
```
5 Q—KN7ch       K—B4
```
If 5 . . . K—R4; 6 Q—KR7ch.
```
6 Q—Q7ch        Resigns
```
At last White wins the Queen.

770
```
1 R—B7!         QxR
2 Q—R7ch        Resigns
```
White wins the Queen.

771
```
1 RxB!          PxR
2 BxBP          QxB/Q5
3 QxQ           RxQ
4 BxR and wins
```
White is a Pawn ahead.

772
```
1 Q—N7ch!       KxR
```
If 1 . . . Q—N3; 2 R—KN4ch
wins the Queen.
```
2 QxRPch        K—N5
4 P—KR3ch       K—B4
4 Q—R7ch and wins
```
White wins the Queen.

773
```
1 NxN           QxN
2 B—B3          N—Q4
3 NxN           PxN
4 BxP           ....
```
White wins the Rook.

774
```
1 Q—K8ch        K—N4
2 P—B4ch        K—B3
```
If 2 . . . K—N5; 3 Q—K2 mate.
```
3 Q—KR8ch       ....
```
White wins the Queen.

775
```
1 ....          B—KN5
```
White cannot play 2 P—B3.
```
2 Q—Q2          BxR
```
Black has won the Exchange.

776
```
1 ....          QxQch
2 KxQ           R—Q8ch
3 K—K2          R—K8ch
```
Black wins the Rook.

777
```
1 ....          NxB
2 QxN           B—K3
```
Black wins the Exchange.

778
```
1 ....          R—K4ch
```
If now 2 K—B6?, B—Q2 mate.
```
2 K—B4          B—K7ch
```
Black wins the Knight.

238 · SOLUTIONS ·

779
1	NxP!
2 NxN	BxN
3 RxB	RxP

Threatens . . . R—N8ch and mate next move.
4 N—Q2	RxP

Threatens 5 . . . R—R8ch and 6 . . . R—N7 mate.
5 NxP	R—R8ch

Followed by . . . RxR and Black has won the Exchange.

780
1	Q—R7!

Threatening . . . Q—R8 mate.
2 P—B3	B—B6

Black wins the Exchange.

781
1 B—N6!	BxB

If 1 . . . P—K8/Q; 2 B—R7 mate.
2 KxB	P—K8/Q
3 P—B7 mate	

782
1 NxP!	N—K1

If 1 . . . PxN; 2 QxN!, PxQ; 3 R—KN1ch, K—R1; 4 BxP mate.
2 N—B6ch!	PxN
3 R—KN1ch	K—R1
4 QxPch!	NxQ
5 BxN mate	

783
1 P—N4!	R—R6ch
2 K—B4	R—R5
3 RxB!	PxR
4 KxP	Resigns

Black is helpless against 5 P—N5ch and 6 RxP mate.

784
1 NxB	PxN
2 RxPch!	QxR
3 NxPch	....

White wins the Queen.

785
1 B—R6ch!	KxB
2 Q—Q2ch	Resigns

White wins Black's Queen.

786
1 BxP!	QxB

If 1 . . . R—N1 White replies as in the main line.
2 N—Q5	....

Threatening 3 NxR mate. Black has no good defense.

787
1 K—Q6!	P—Q7
2 K—B7!	P—Q8/Q
3 R—QR6ch!	PxR
4 P—N6ch	K—R1
5 P—N7ch	K—R2
6 P—N8/Q mate	

788
1 R—Q8ch!	Resigns

If 1 . . . RxR; 2 BxQ. If 1 . . . KxR; 2 N—N7ch and 3 NxQ.

789
1 N—N6ch!	Resigns

If 1 . . . RPxN; 2 Q—R8 mate. King moves by Black allow 2 NxQ.

790   Black, though two pieces down, seems to have things all his own way. If 1 K—B1, Q—B7 mate. If 1 K—N2, Q—B7ch; 2 K—R3, Qx RPch; 3 KxN, Q—R4 mate. If 1 N—Q4, RxN with a devastating discovered check to come. But:
1 N—N6!	QxNch
2 Q—Q4ch!	RxQ

Or 2 . . . QxQch; 3 NxQ, RxN; 4 BxN and White remains a piece ahead.
3 RxQ	Resigns

White wins another piece.

791
1 NxRP!	KxN
2 BxN	P—KN3
3 QxPch!	PxQ
4 BxR mate	

792
1 R—N6!	PxR
2 RPxPch	RxP
3 PxRch and wins	

White has a mating attack.

793
1 NxP!	PxN
2 BxB	KxB
3 QxBP	N—B2

Forced.
4 R—B1	R—K2
5 R—B5	Q—N3

Or 5 . . . Q—N5; 6 Q—Q6, R—Q2; 7 Q—K5ch, P—B3; 8 QxN! White gets a decisive material advantage.
6 QxQ	PxQ
7 RxN!	RxR
8 BxR and wins	

White is a Pawn ahead.

794
1 N—B7!	KxN
2 QxPch!	K—N3

If 2 . . . KxQ; 3 N—N5 mate!
3 P—KN4!	B—K5
4 N—R4 mate	

795
1 B—N5!	QxB
2 RxPch!	KxR
3 Q—R5ch	B—R3
4 QxB mate	

796 1 P—K4! BxN
If 1 . . . QxP; 2 B—R6!, Qx N/K4; 3 Q—R8 mate. Thus White's first move serves to develop White's Bishop.

  2 B—R6ch K—K1
  3 PxB QxP
  4 Q—N8ch K—Q2
  5 R—Q1ch Resigns

797 1 BxPch! KxB
  2 N—K6! N/Q2—K4
If 2 . . . KxN; 3 Q—Q5ch, K— B3; 4 Q—KB5 mate.
  3 NxQ Resigns

798 Black is threatening . . . Q— B8ch followed by mate.
  1 R—B8ch! BxR
If 1 . . . K—B2; 2 Q—B7ch leads to mate.
  2 Q—K8ch R—B1
  3 RxPch! KxR
If 3 . . . K—R1; 4 R—R7ch, K—N1; 5 Q—N6 mate.
  4 Q—N6ch K—R1
  5 Q—R7 mate

799 1 N—QN5! PxN
  2 N—Q6ch QxN
If 2 . . . K—K2; 3 RxPch!, NxR; 4 QxNch, K—Q1; 5 Q—K8 mate.
  3 RxQ Resigns

800 1 R—B7! R/R6—R1
If 1 . . . R/B1xR; 2 R—N8 followed by R—KB8 mate. If 1 . . . R/R6xR; 2 RxR with the same result.
If 1 . . . R—K1; 2 R—N6! followed by 3 RxQP after Black saves his Bishop.
  2 R/N3—QB3! RxR
  3 NxR R—R8
  4 N—K6! Resigns
He is helpless against 5 R—B8 and 6 R—B8 mate.

801 1 B—KR6ch! KxB
  2 RxPch K—N2
  3 QR—R1 R—R1
Despair. He had no good line against the mating threat 4 R—R7ch etc.
  4 RxR QxR
  5 RxQ RxR
  6 Q—QN3 . . . .
White has a winning material advantage.

802 1 N—Q7ch K—B1
  2 N—N6 dbl ch K—N1
  3 Q—B8ch! RxQ
  4 N—Q7 mate

803 1 N—R6ch! K—R1
If 1 . . . PxN; 2 BxP!, QxB; 3 QxPch, K—R1; 4 QxRch wins.
  2 NxPch K—N1
  3 Q—N3! Q—K2
  4 N—R6ch K—R1
  5 R—B7 Resigns

804 1 K—K3! Resigns
If 1 . . . P—KR4; 2 N—K4ch, K—B4, 3 N—R4 mate.

805 1 . . . . B—Q6!
  2 BxB . . . .
If 2 Q—Q1, Q—B7ch; 3 K—R1, BxB wins.
  2 . . . . Q—K6ch
  3 K—R1 . . . .
If 3 K—B1, N—R7 mate.
  3 . . . . Q—K8ch
And mate follows.

806 1 . . . . N—R5!
  2 PxN . . . .
If 2 KxN, R—QR8 mate.
  2 . . . . RxQ
  Resigns

807 1 . . . . BxN!
If now 2 RxQ, R—Q8ch leads to mate.
  2 QxRch . . . .
So that if 2 . . . RxQ; 3 RxQ, PxR; 4 PxB with drawing chances.
  2 . . . . K—R2!
  Resigns
White's Queen is lost: if 3 R/ B4—B1, Q—R5; 4 P—KR3, RxQ, etc.

808 1 . . . . B—QR3!
  2 QxB Q—Q7
Threatens . . . QxP mate, and also . . . . BxNch.
  3 N—K2 Q—K6ch
  4 K—R1 Q—B6ch
  5 B—N2 N/K5—B7ch
  6 K—N1 N—R6ch
  7 BxN Q—B7ch
  8 K—R1 QxP mate

809 1 . . . . R—R8ch!
  2 KxR PxP
  Resigns
Black threatens to mate with . . .

R—KR1ch and he also threatens
. . . PxR/Qch.

810
1	R—B8ch!
2 KxR	R—K8ch!
3 NxR	QxN mate

811
1	N—KN5!
2 BxQ	BxPch
3 RxB	PxRch
4 K—B1	R—R8ch
5 K—K2	RxQ
6 KN—Q2	N—Q5ch!
7 KxR	N—K6ch
8 K—B1	N—K7 mate

812
1	N—B6ch
2 K—B1	Q—N4ch
3 K—N1	N—Q7ch
4 K—B1	N—N6 dbl ch
5 K—N1	Q—B8ch!
6 RxQ	N—Q7 mate

813
1	R—R5ch!
2 PxR	P—N5 mate

814
1	N/Q2xP!
2 PxN	BxPch
3 K—R1	NxPch!
4 PxN	Q—R4ch

And mate next move.

815
1	RxP!
2 PxR	BxPch

If now 3 QxB, NxNch wins the
Queen.
3 K—B1	QxPch!
4 KxQ	B—KR6 mate

816
1	P—KN4!

If now 2 BxP, NxBP wins. Or if
2 B—K3, Q—B6 (or 2 . . . N—K4)
wins.
2 P—B3	Q—B4ch!
3 K—N2	Q—B7ch
4 K—R3	QxRPch!
5 KxN	RxBch!
6 PxR	Q—R5 mate

817
1	B—K6!

Threatens 2 . . . BxPch! or 2
. . . P—N6!
2 PxB	P—N6
3 R—Q7	P—B7ch
4 K—B1	P—R7
Resigns	

For after 5 K—N2 Black queens
one Pawn and then the other.

818
1	N—B6ch!
2 K—R1	....

If 2 PxN, PxP and wins because
of the threat of . . . Q—N5ch.
2	N—N5
3 QxNP	QxBP!

The Queen cannot be captured,
and meanwhile Black threatens . . .
Q—N8ch!

819 After the promising-looking 1
. . . B—N6 White has 2 RxRch,
RxR; 3 R—QN1! So:
1	P—K4!
2 RxB	RxR
3 PxR	PxB

Threatens . . . R—B8.
4 R—QN1	R—B7ch
5 K—K1	R—B8ch

Black queens the Pawn.

820
1	KRxB!
2 RxR	QxP!
3 PxQ	....

Or 3 K—N1, N—B6ch!; 4 PxN,
K—R1 and the threat of . . . R—
N1ch decides.
3	BxPch
4 K—N1	N—B6ch
5 K—R1	B—N7ch!
6 KxB	NxRch

Followed by . . . NxQ with a
winning game.

821
1	QxR
2 QxR	Q—R1ch

Black mates next move.

822
1	P—N4!
2 PxP	....

If 2 Q—R5, B—N3 wins the
Queen.
2	PxP
3 QxNP	RxR
Resigns	

823
1 Q—N3ch!	R—B2

If 1 . . . K—R1; 2 N—N6ch
forces mate.
2 NxR	QxN
3 R—K8ch	B—B1
4 B—B4	Resigns

White will be a Rook ahead.

824 Black, who was a piece down,
has just played . . . P—N6ch winning White's Queen. But . . .
1 K—K3!	QxQ
2 P—B3!	....

Now Black must give back his Queen, for if 2 . . . Q—R4?; 3 N—B6ch wins. White will win the weak King Knight Pawn, with a Pawn to the good.

825
1 PxP!	RxB
2 PxRPch	NxRP
3 QxNch	K—B1
4 Q—R8ch	K—K2
5 QxPch	K—Q2
6 R—Q1ch	K—B1
7 Q—K8ch	K—N2
8 QxKBPch	Resigns

White wins the Rook.

826
1 N—B3!	QxR
2 N—K5!	....

This move stops the renewed threat of mate, attacks Black's Queen, and also threatens 3 N—Q7 mate.

2	QxB
3 NxQch	Resigns

827 Despite Black's threat to win rapidly with . . . R—R3, White plays:

1 PxN!	BxP

If 1 . . . R—R3; 2 PxPch!, K—N1; 3 N—B6ch, KxP; 4 NxRch, K—B1; 5 QxBch!, KxQ; 6 KR—Q1ch followed by 7 B—B3 and the White King escapes.

2 NxB!	RxQ
3 KRxR!	PxN
4 P—B5!	R—N1
5 QR—N1!	Resigns

Else 6 B—R6 mate.

828
1 Q—R2ch!	BxQ
2 R—N2ch!	KxR
3 RxQ	Resigns

829
1 RxB!	QxR
2 N—N6!	Resigns

If 2 . . . RxQ; 3 NxQ and both Rooks are en prise.

830 Black threatens . . . Q—N8 mate.

1 B—K3!	QxB

On such moves as . . . Q—N5 or . . . Q—Q3 White wins with Q—N4ch.

2 Q—N4ch	Q—K3

If 2 . . . N—Q2; 3 R—QR8 mate. If 2 . . . R—Q2; 3 R—KR8ch and mate follows.

3 QxQch	PxQ
4 RxP mate	

831
1 R—K8ch	B—B1

If 1 . . . K—R2; 2 Q—Q3ch wins.

2 RxBch!	KxR
3 N—B5 dis ch	K—N1
4 Q—B8ch!	Resigns

If 4 . . . KxQ; 5 R—Q8 mate.

832
1 R—K4ch!	K—B1

If 1 . . . KxP; 2 N—K5ch wins. If 1 . . . K—Q2; 2 QxP wins.

2 NxP!	QxN

If 2 . . . QxQ; 3 R—K8ch, RxR; 4 PxR/Q mate.

3 R—K8ch!	RxR
4 QxPch!	KxQ

If 4 . . . K—K2; 5 P—B8/Q dbl ch and mate follows.

5 PxR/Nch!	K—B1
6 NxQ	Resigns

833 In the face of Black's crushing threat of . . . N—B6ch, White finds a clever resource:

1 PxP!	N—B6ch
2 QxN!	PxQ
3 N—B5ch	K—N1!

If 3 . . . K—R1?; 4 P—N7ch, K—N1; 5 N—R6 mate.

4 N—K7ch	K—N2
5 N—B5ch	K—N1

Drawn by perpetual check.

834
1 R—R6!	RxR
2 P—R8/Qch	RxQ
3 P—N5!	Drawn

Black cannot relieve the stalemate position.

835 With a piece down, White manages to find a perpetual check:

1 Q—Q8ch	K—R2
2 R—Q3!	Q—K8

If 2 . . . QxR White has a perpetual check by 3 Q—R5ch etc.

3 R—Q1!	QxR
4 Q—R5ch	Drawn

Black cannot escape from the perpetual check.

836
1 Q—KB2!	Drawn

After 1 . . . QxQ White is stalemated.

837 Black is just about to checkmate.

	1 R—B6ch!	PxR
	2 QxBPch	K—R2
	3 Q—R8ch	Drawn

White has a perpetual check.

838 1 Q—B6!   PxQ
     2 RxR mate

839 White is the Exchange down and he cannot play 1 QxQ because of . . . Q—B4ch and mate next move. Yet he draws:

	1 Q—KN8ch!	KxQ
	2 Q—K8ch!	K—R2
	3 Q—KN8ch!	K—R3
	4 Q—R7ch!	K—N4
	5 Q—R6ch!	Drawn

After 5 . . . KxQ White is stalemated.

840 White's Queen is apparently lost, for if the Queen moves, Black checkmates.

     1 R—N5!   . . . .

If now 1 . . . QxR; 2 QxRch and wins. And if 1 . . . Q—K3 or . . . Q—B5; 2 Q—N7 mate.

     1 . . . .   R—K1!

If now 2 RxQ, R—K8 mate.

     2 R—N1!   R—KN1!

Black's best, as he is a piece down.

     3 R—N5!   R—K1!

Drawn by repetition.

841

	1	Q—K8ch!
	2 KxR	Q—R5ch
	3 K—B5	Q—R4ch
	4 K—K6	Q—K1ch
	Drawn	

White cannot escape the perpetual check.

842 Though Black is a piece ahead, the pressure is troublesome. The simplest way out is:

     1 . . . .   QxRch!
     2 QxQ   B—N5! and wins

White must either play 3 QxRch or else give up his Queen after . . . R—Q8ch. In either case, Black remains a piece ahead.

843

     1 . . . .   P—K7!
     2 RxP   . . . .

If 2 R—B2, B—N6 wins the Exchange.

     2 . . . .   RxR
     3 QxR   NxP and wins

After White's Queen moves, Black plays . . . NxNch with a Pawn up and much the better position.

844 1 . . . .   RxP!

If now 2 KxR, Q—R2ch; 3 K—N1, R—R1; 4 P—B3, P—N6! forcing mate.

     2 PxP   RxPch
     3 K—B1   RxPch!

If now 4 K—N1, R—N7ch; 5 K—B1, N—K6 dis ch and mate follows.

     4 KxR   Q—B7ch
     5 K—Q3   N—N7 mate

845 White threatens BxR or QxN in addition to QxP mate.

     1 . . . .   N/Q4—B3!
     2 BxB   . . . .

If 2 BxR, Q—Q4; 3 P—B3, QxQPch and wins.

     2 . . . .   RxBP!
     Resigns

Black is well ahead in material, and if 3 RxR, QxQP is crushing.

846

	1	RxKRPch!
	2 KxR	Q—K3ch!
	3 QxQ	Drawn

Black is stalemated.

847 1 N—QR4   Resigns

848 1 N—B4   Resigns

849 1 N—K3   Resigns

850 1 RxB!   QxR
     2 N—B3   Resigns

There is nothing to be done against 3 R—N1.

851 1 BxPch   NxB
     2 N—N6   Resigns

852 1 B—KN5!   BxN
     2 Q—Q2!   QxP
     3 B—N5ch   Resigns

853 1 . . . .   N—R5!
     Resigns

854 1 . . . .   P—B4
     2 Q—K3   P—B5
     Resigns

855 1 . . . .   N—Q4

If now 2 QxKP, NxPch.

2	Q—Q6	NxPch
3	K—Q2	P—K4!
	Resigns	

856 1 ....   B—N5
Resigns
If 2 N—KN1, P—B6 traps the
Bishop.

857

1	....	P—KN4
2	B—N3	P—KR4
3	N—R2	P—R5
	Resigns	

858

1	....	P—KN4!
2	B—N3	P—N5
3	N—N1	BxP
	Resigns	

859 1 R—B7!   Resigns
After Black's Pawn moves are exhausted, he must move a piece,
losing a piece.

860 1 P—R4!   Resigns
After Black's Pawn moves are
exhausted, he must play . . . Q—K1
or . . . K—K1. In either event
P—N5 thereupon wins a piece.

861 1 R—N5!   Resigns
After Black's Pawn moves are
exhausted, he loses his Queen.

862 1 Q—K7ch!   Q—N4
If 1 . . . P—N4; 2 Q—K1ch
and mate follows.

2	Q—K4ch!	Q—N5
3	Q—K3!	Resigns

Black cannot avoid mate. Thus,
if 3 . . . Q—N4; 4 Q—KR3 mate.
Or if 3 . . . P—N4; 4 Q—K1ch
forcing mate. And if 3 . . . Q—B4;
4 Q—KN3 mate.

863

1	RxR!	RxR
2	P—KR4!	P—R3
3	K—N2	P—KN4

Hoping to play . . . K—N3.

4	P—R5!	Resigns

Sooner or later the Black King
will have to give up protection of
the Rook.

864

1	R—R3ch!	PxRch
2	K—B3	P—N5ch
3	K—B4	P—N6
4	PxP mate	

865

1	....	B—B8ch
2	K—N4	P—R4ch
4	K—R4	B—K6!
	Resigns	

If 4 P—N4, B—B7 mate. If
White's Knight moves, then . . .
B—N4 mate.

866 1 ....   B—B5!
Now Black can win in many
ways, for example:

2	K—N4	K—Q4
3	K—R4	K—B4
	Resigns	

Black wins the Queen Knight
Pawn.

867 1 ....   K—K6!
White is powerless against the
following mate pattern.

2	RxP	R—Q8ch
3	R—N1	K—B7!
4	RxR	B—N7 mate

868

1	....	R—KN1!
2	R—KN1	....

If 2 P—B6 the Bishop is lost. If
the Rook moves anywhere else along
the rank, 2 . . . QxBP wins. If 2
R—B2, Q—R8 mate. If 2 BxP,
R—N7ch leads to mate.

2	....	RxB!
3	QxR	Q—Q3ch
	Resigns	

Black comes out a piece ahead.

869 1 ....   B—R3!
If now 2 BxB, Q—B7; 3 R—
KN1, Q—R5ch; 4 K—N2, Q—
N6ch! 5 K—B1, Q—B7 mate.

2	Q—B3	B—Q6!
3	P—R4	B—K5!
4	Q—B1	Q—N7!
	Resigns	

White can do nothing against the
maneuver 5 . . . Q—N2 and 6 . . .
Q—KR2 mate.

870 1 ....   P—R3!
Resigns
If 1 K—R2, R/B4—B6 wins the
Queen. If 1 P—KN4, R/B4—B6;
2 BxR, R—R7 mate. If 1 B—B1,
BxN wins. If 1 R—Q1, R—K7 wins.

871 1 P—N4ch!   KxP
If 1 . . . K—N3; 2 R—N7ch,
K—R3; 3 R—R1 mate.

2	R—N7ch	K—B6

If 2 . . . K—B4; 3 R—N5 mate.
  3 N—K4ch   K—B7
If 3 . . . K—B5; 4 R—Q4 mate.
  4 R/N7—N1! Resigns
There follows 5 R/Q1—B1 mate.

872 1 Q—N5ch!   N—Q2
  If 1 . . . QxQ or 1 . . . N—B3;
2 N—B6 mate.
    2 KR—K1!   . . . .
  Threatens N—B6 mate or N—Q6
mate.
    2 . . . .   B—N5
    3 N—B6 dbl ch K—B1
    4 NxNch   RxN
    5 Q—K5!   Resigns
  He cannot meet the triple mate
threat.

873 1 Q—N4ch   K—Q6
    2 Q—K2ch   K—B7
    3 P—Q3 dis ch   KxB
  If 3 . . . K—N8; 4 Castles wins.
    4 Castles, mate!

874 1 B—N5!   QxB
  If 1 . . . P—QB3; 2 PxP, PxP;
3 BxP, QxB; 4 RxNch wins the
Queen.
    2 QxB   P—KB3
    3 QR—K1!   PxN
    4 RxNch   K—Q1
    5 QxNP   K—B1
    6 Q—N4ch   K—Q1
    7 P—QR4!   Resigns
  Black's Queen can no longer stop
mate.

875 1 BxPch!   RxB
  If 1 . . . K—B1; 2 N—N6ch
wins the Queen.
    2 RxR   KxR
    3 Castles   P—B4
    4 R—R1ch   K—N1
    5 R—R8ch! Resigns
  After 5 . . . KxR; 6 N—N6ch
wins the Queen.

876 1 RxP!   KxR
    2 Q—B6ch   B—Q3
    3 N—N5ch and wins
  White regains the sacrificed Rook
with a much superior position.

877 1 RxP!   KxR
  If 1 . . . QxR; 2 B—N5 wins the
Queen.
    2 B—N5ch   K—N2

If 2 . . . K—K4; 3 B—K7 dis
ch leads to mate.
    3 Q—R6ch   K—N1
    4 R—KB1   R—KB1
    5 B—KB6   QxB
    6 RxQ   Resigns
  The threat was 7 RxNch, RPxR;
8 QxP mate.

878 1 R—B7ch!   KxR
    2 Q—K6ch   K—N2
  If 2 . . . K—B1; 3 R—KB1ch
leads to mate.
    3 Q—K7ch   K—R3
    4 N—B5 mate
Or 4 N—B3 mate.

879 1 QxBch!   NxQ
    2 N—K6 mate

880 1 RxB!   QxR
    2 B—N4ch   K—K1
    3 QxPch!   PxQ
    4 B—N6 mate

881 1 QxPch!   NxQ
    2 BxBP mate

882 1 RxPch!   K—Q2
  If 1 . . . PxR; 2 Q—N7ch wins.
    2 RxBch!   KxR
    3 N—B5 dbl ch K—K3
    4 R—K3ch   K—Q2
    5 R—K7ch   Resigns
  Mate is unavoidable.

883 1 P—N4ch!   PxP
    2 RPxPch   K—R5
    3 QxRPch!   QxQ
    4 K—R2!   Resigns
  There follows 5 B—B2 mate.

884 1 BxBPch!   KxB
    2 Q—N7 mate

885 1 RxBch!   KxR
    2 Q—B8ch   K—K2
    3 NxPch   Resigns
  Black must give up his Queen.

886 1 RxB!   PxR
    2 QxP   R—KB1
    3 QxNPch   K—Q2
    4 B—K6 mate

887 1 B—N6ch!   K—B1
  If 1 . . . PxB; 2 PxPch, KxP;
3 QxKPch, B—B3; 4 R—N3ch,
K—R2; 5 RxQP and wins.
    2 QxKP   PxB

3 PxP Resigns
Black cannot meet the double mating threat.

888 1 BxPch! KxB
  2 N—N5ch K—K1
If 2 . . . K—B3; 3 Q—K6 mate.
  3 Q—K6 Resigns
Mate is forced.

889 1 N—B7! KxN
  2 R—KB1ch K—K1
  3 RxBch! Resigns
Mate is forced.

890 1 Q—R6ch! NxQ
  2 BxN mate
(More pleasing than 1 B—KR6ch etc.)

891 1 QR—Q1! BxQ
  2 R—Q3 mate

892 1 N—N5! N—R4
White threatened 2 NxBP, KxN; 3 N—N6 dis ch.
  2 Q—R5! P—N3
  3 N—B6ch! NxN
  4 BxPch K—K2
  5 B—B5ch Resigns

893 1 P—B6 dis ch! PxQ
  2 B—K6ch K—K1
  3 P—B7 mate

894 1 NxKBP! N—B3
If 1 . . . RxN; 2 Q—N6.
  2 QxKP! NxR
  3 N—Q6ch K—Q1
  4 B—R5! Resigns
If 4 . . . QxB; 5 QxR mate.

895 1 NxP! PxN
If 1 . . . BxN; 2 Q—Q8 mate.
If 1 . . . QxN; 2 R—B8ch! forces mate.
  2 R—B8ch! K—B2
If 2 . . . BxR; 3 Q—Q8ch leads to mate.
  3 RxR PxB
Or 3 . . . KxB; 4 Q—B3ch wins.
  4 Q—R5ch K—K2
  5 Q—QB5ch K—B2
  6 RxPch K—N1
  7 Q—K7 Resigns

896 1 RxP! KxR
  2 R—KB1ch K—N2
  3 B—R6ch! KxB
  4 R—B7 Q—Q1

  5 RxPch! KxR
  6 QxNP mate

897 1 Q—B7ch! NxQ
  2 PxN mate

898 1 N—K7! . . . .
If the Knight is captured, 2 RxNch! leads to mate.
  1 . . . . Q—B3
  2 N—R7ch! Resigns
If 2 . . . RxN; 3 QxN mate.

899 1 RxBch! PxR
  2 N—Q3ch! PxN
  3 P—KB4 mate

900 1 Q—Q6 Q—Q1
  2 R—N8 B—K1
  3 RxB! Resigns
If 3 . . . QxB; 4 Q—B7 mate.

901 1 . . . . RxB!
  2 QxR R—R4ch!
  3 KxR Q—R6ch
  4 K—N5 P—R3ch
  5 K—B4 P—N4ch
  6 K—K5 Q—K3 mate

902 1 . . . . N—R4!
Threatens . . . N—B5 mate.
  2 PxN Q—B6ch
  3 K—R4 B—Q2 mate

903 1 . . . . BxQP!
  2 PxB RxP
  3 Q—N4 RxBch
  4 KxR B—N5ch
  5 K—B1 R—K8ch
  6 Q—Q1 Q—QB3ch
And mate next move.

904 1 . . . . N—Q5ch
  2 K—K3 N/K2—B4 mate

905 1 . . . . B—N5ch!
  2 PxB Q—K6ch
  3 K—B2 NxP mate

906 1 . . . . N—Q2
  2 BxN PxB
  3 Any N—N3 mate

907 1 BxRPch! KxB
  2 Q—R5ch K—N1
  3 BxP! KxB
  4 Q—N5ch K—R1
  5 R—Q4 Resigns
He has no good defense to the threat of R—R4ch.

908 1 NxP! QxN
If 1 . . . PxQ; 2 NxBch, K—R1;
3 RxP dis ch, P—B3; 4 RxP mate.
If 1 . . . PxN; 2 QxRPch! leads
to mate.
    2 Q—R6! B—Q1
    3 RxN! Resigns
White forces mate.

909 1 NxQBP! PxN
    2 R—N8ch! K—K2
    3 QxPch K—Q2
    4 Q—B8ch Resigns
White mates in two more moves.

910 1 RxPch! K—K1
Surprising; but if 1 . . . PxR; 2
Q—R7ch, K—B1 (or 2 . . . K—K3;
3 N—B4 mate); 3 Q—R8ch, K—
K2; 4 R—R7ch and White mates
in three more moves.
    2 R—B8ch Resigns

911 1 BxPch! KxB
    2 Q—R5ch K—N1
    3 QxPch K—R1
    4 N—B6! Resigns

912 1 QxP! Resigns
If 1 . . . PxQ; 2 B—R7 mate.

913 1 BxN! PxQ
If 1 . . . BxB; 2 QxRP wins
easily without sacrifices.
    2 RxBch K—B1
If 2 . . . K—R1 White mates on
the move.
    3 R—R7! Resigns
White has 4 R—R8 mate.

914 1 RxRPch! KxR
    2 RxPch! RxR
    3 QxPch K—R1
    4 QxR Resigns
If 4 . . . N—N2; 5 P—K6.

915 1 B—KR6! B—K4
    2 NxB! BxQ
    3 NxBch K—R1
    4 B—N7ch! KxB
    5 NxRch Resigns

916 1 RxP! KxR
    2 R—KN1ch K—R2
Or 2 . . . K—R1; 3 NxN, BxN,
4 N—K4!, BxB; 5 QxBch, P—B3;
6 NxKBP winning.
    3 NxNch BxN
    4 B—K4ch K—R1

    5 Q—R5 B—N2
    6 RxB! Resigns
If 6 . . . KxR; 7 N—Q5 dis ch
leads to mate.

917 1 B—B6! BxB
    2 P—K5 . . . .
Threatens 3 QxRP mate.
    2 . . . . NxB
    3 PxB Resigns
He is helpless against Q—N7
mate.

918 1 RxP! KxR
    2 Q—R5ch K—N1
    3 BxN Resigns
Black has no good counter to the
threat of 4 Q—R7 mate.

919 1 NxP! RxPch
If 1 . . . NxN; 2 RPxP wins
easily.
    2 QxR! PxQ
    3 NxNch K—R2
    4 B—Q1! Resigns
For B—B2 mate follows.

920 1 QxBPch! PxQ
    2 B—QR6 mate

921 1 B—KB4! Q—R4
    2 NxPch K—Q2
    3 B—QN5 mate

922 1 Q—R6! QxRch
    2 B—B1 Resigns
Black must give up his Queen to
stop Q—N7 mate.

923 1 R—R7ch! K—B1
If 1 . . . KxR; 2 Q—R4ch, K—
N2; 3 Q—R6 mate.
    2 Q—R8ch! N—B1
    3 QxNch Resigns

924 1 NxKBP! RxN
    2 QxPch K—B1
    3 BxPch B—N2
    4 Q—R7! . . . .
Threatens 5 Q—R8 mate.
    4 . . . . N—K2
    5 Q—R8ch N—N1
    6 B—R7 Resigns

925 1 N—K6! BxN
    2 QxPch! KxQ
    3 R—R3ch Resigns
It is mate next move.

926

1 RxB!	PxR
2 Q—N3ch	K—R1
3 B—K7!	Resigns

He is helpless against QBxP mate.

927

1 NxP!	BxN
2 QxRPch!	KxQ
3 RxR mate	

928

1 RxP!	KxR
2 R—R1ch	K—N3
3 Q—N4	B—Q2

Or 3 . . . P—B3; 4 Q—R5ch, K—B4; 5 N—Q4ch with a mating attack.

4 P—B5ch!	BxP
5 Q—R5 mate	

929

1 RxPch!	KxR
2 Q—R1ch	K—N2
3 B—R6ch	K—B3
4 Q—R4ch	K—K4
5 QxNch	K—B4
6 Q—B4 mate	

930

1 RxP!	N—B3

If 1 . . . PxR, 2 QxPch and mate next move.

2 N—K5	P—B4
3 BxPch!	KxB
4 NxPch!	Resigns

If 4 . . . RxN; 5 QxP mate.

931

1 QxPch!	RxQ
2 R—N8 mate	

932

1 RxBch!	BPxR
2 R—B7ch!	KxR
3 QxRPch	K—K3

If 3 . . . K—B1; 4 N—B4 with mate to follow.

4 QxNPch	K—K4
5 Q—N7ch	KxP

Or 5 . . . K—K3; 6 N—B4 mate.

6 N—B6ch	Resigns

White wins the Queen.

933

1 N—B5ch!	PxN

If 1 . . . K—R1; 2 RxPch!, KxR; 3 Q—R1ch wins.

2 RxPch!	KxR
3 Q—R5ch	N—R3

If 3 . . . K—N2; 4 P—N6 forces mate.

4 QxNch	K—N1
5 Q—N6ch	K—R1

6 B—K3	. . . .

Followed by 7 R—R1 mate.

934 White opens the King Knight file with telling effect:

1 QxN!	BxN
2 BxB!	PxQ
3 R—KN1ch	K—R1
4 B—KN7ch	K—N1
5 B—KB6 dis ch	K—B1
6 R—N2!	R—K2
7 QR—KN1	K—K1
8 B—B6ch!	Resigns

White mates next move.

935

1 R—R7ch!	KxR
2 QxPch	K—R1
3 R—R1ch	Resigns

White mates next move.

936

1 B—B6!	P—KR3

If 1 . . . PxB; 2 R—Q3!, NxB; 3 R—KR3 forces mate. If 1 . . . NxB; 2 Q—N5, P—KN3; 3 Q—R6 with the same result.

2 Q—N6!	. . . .

Followed by 3 QxNP mate.

937

1 QxRch!	KxQ
2 P—K7 mate	

938

1 RxPch!	KxR
2 Q—R5ch	K—N1
3 B—R6	. . . .

Threatening 4 Q—N5ch and mate next move.

3	N—K2
4 P—K6!	NxP
5 R—N3ch!	Resigns

If 5 . . . NxR; 6 Q—N5ch and 7 Q—N7 mate.

939

1 P—R6ch!	K—N1
2 Q—B6	. . . .

And 3 Q—N7 mate.

940

1 B—B8!	RxB
2 R—R8ch!	KxR
3 QxR/B8ch	R—N1
4 Q—B6ch!	R—N2
5 Q—R4ch!	K—N1
6 Q—K8ch	. . . .

White mates next move!

941

1 RxPch	K—B1

If 1 . . . K—R1; 2 RxRP dbl ch, K—N1; 3 R—R8 mate.

2 R—N8ch!	KxR
3 R—N1ch	K—B1
4 B—N7ch!	K—N1

5 B—B6 dis ch   K—B1
6 R—N8ch!   KxR
7 Q—N2ch   K—B1
8 Q—N7 mate

942   1 RxP!   ....
If now 1 . . . BxB; 2 QxPch,
B—N2; 3 R—R8ch!, KxR; 4 Q—
R7 mate. Or 2 . . . R—N2; 3 Q—
K6ch forcing mate.
      1 ....   KxR
      2 QxPch   K—N1
      3 R—R1!   Resigns
Because of 4 R—R8ch!

943   1 BxP!   B—B2
If 1 . . . PxB; 2 QxPch, K—R1;
3 N—N6ch winning the Queen.
      2 BxPch   Resigns
If 2 . . . BxB; 3 NxB! winning
the Rook with a discovered check.

944   1 Q—N4ch   Q—N3
If 1 . . . K—R1; 2 Q—N7 mate.
      2 N—K7ch   Resigns
White wins the Queen.

945   1 NxP!   PxN
      2 QxP   ....
If now 2 . . . B—K1; 3 B—Q5ch
wins. Or 2 . . . R—B3; 3 RxR,
PxR; 4 B—Q5ch etc.
      2 ....   P—K3
      3 B—K4!   R—B4
      4 RxR!   PxR
      5 B—Q5ch   Resigns

946   1 BxPch!   KxB
      2 R—B7ch   K—R3
If 2 . . . K—N1; 3 R—N7ch, K—
B1; 4 Q—KB1ch, K—K1; 5 Q—
B7ch followed by mate.
      3 B—K3ch!   RxB
If 3 . . . K—R4; 4 P—N4ch wins
easily.
      4 Q—B6ch   Resigns
White mates quickly.

947   1 RxB!   RxR
      2 QxRPch   R—R2
      3 QxR mate

948   1 Q—R6   Resigns
He is helpless against 2 Q—N7
mate.

949   1 RxP!   KxR
      2 Q—B7ch   K—R3
      3 B—N7ch   K—N4
      4 P—B4ch   K—R4
      5 P—N3   N—R3

6 N—K5 dis ch!   NxQ
7 B—K2ch   B—N5
8 BxB mate

950   1 RxB!   KxR
      2 B—K5ch   K—R3
      3 N—B7ch   K—R4
      4 B—K2ch   K—R5
      5 B—N3ch   K—R6
      6 N—N5 mate

951   1 NxP!   KxN
      2 B—R5ch!   KxB
      3 N—N3ch   K—R5
      4 Q—K4ch   ....
White mates next move.

952   1 RxP!   RxR
      2 RxR   R—B2
If 2 . . . KxR; 3 Q—R5ch and
mate in two more moves.
      3 R—R6   N—B5
      4 RxPch   Resigns
White has won two Pawns and
maintains the attack.

953   1 RxRP!   KxR
      2 R—R1ch   K—N1
      3 R—R8ch   K—B2
      4 Q—B6ch   K—K1
      5 RxRch   K—Q2
      6 Q—N7ch   B—B2
      7 QxB mate

954   1 Q—K8ch!   KxR
If 1 . . . NxQ; 2 R—N8 mate.
      2 Q—B7ch   K—R1
      3 B—KR6   Resigns
Black is helpless against Q—N7
mate.

955   1 P—B6!   PxP
If 1 . . . R/Q2—Q1; 2 QxP mate.
      2 B—R6ch   K—Q1
      3 Q—N8 mate

956   1 RxP!   R—Q2
If 1 . . . PxR; 2 B—R6ch, K—
R1; 3 Q—N5 forces mate. If 1 . . .
NxR; 2 QxPch and mate next
move.
      2 R—R8!   Resigns
If 2 . . . KxR; 3 NxBPch wins
the Queen. Meanwhile White threatens 3 B—R6ch! or 3 Q—R4 with
decisive effect.

957   1 Q—N4!   ....
Not 1 Q—Q4, Q—N4.

1 ....   P—KN3
2 Q—Q4   Resigns
Black cannot stop mate, as 2 . . .
P—KB3 is impossible.

958   1 BxPch!   KxB
2 N—N5ch   K—N1
If 2 . . . BxN; 3 PxB dis ch wins
quickly.
3 Q—R5   BxN
4 PxB   K—B1
5 Q—R8ch   K—K2
6 N—N6ch!   PxN
7 QxP mate

959   1 RxPch!   KxR
After 1 . . . K—B1; 2 R—N5
Black cannot hold out very long.
2 Q—N3ch   K—B2
3 R—R7ch   K—K1
4 Q—QN8ch   K—Q2
5 QxNPch   K—Q1
6 QxRch   K—B1
7 Q—B7 mate

960   1 QxNch!   KxQ
2 B—K5 mate

961   1 RxP!   KxR
2 QxNch   K—B1
3 Q—R6ch   K—Q2
4 B—B6 mate

962   1 NxNP!   PxN
White threatened 2 R—R8 mate.
2 Q—B5   N—B3
3 Q—Q6ch   Q—B2
4 R—R8 mate

963   1 RxP!   BxR
If 1 . . . RxR; 2 Q—N5!, B—
QB4; 3 B—B8! and White forces
mate.
2 Q—N5!   B—B6ch
If 2 . . . BxQ; 3 B—N7 mate.
3 K—N1!   RxR
4 QxBch   ....

964   1 QxRP!   Resigns
If 1 . . . PxQ; 2 B—R7 mate.

965   1 BxP!   PxB
2 QxP   N—Q2
3 N—KN5   Q—B3
4 R—R8ch!   KxR
5 Q—R7 mate

966   1 Q—R5   P—KR3
2 QxN   PxN
3 BxNP   Q—K1

4 B—B6   ....
Followed by 5 QxNP mate.

967   1 R—Q7!   QxR
2 QxP!   ....
Without White's first move, Black
could now save himself with . . .
QxRPch!
2 ....   PxQ
3 B—R7 mate

968   1 NxNP!   KxN
2 Q—K5ch   ....
If now 2 . . . P—B3; 3 NxPch,
K—R1; 4 Q—N3 winning Black's
Queen because of the mate threat.
Or 2 . . . B—B3; 3 N—R5ch, K—
N3; 4 NxB, QxN; 5 Q—N3ch,
K—R4; 6 Q—R3ch, Q—R5; 7 P—
KN4ch winning the Queen.
2 ....   K—N1
3 N—R5   Resigns
If 3 . . . P—B3; 4 Q—N3ch wins.

969   1 QxNPch!   KxQ
Or 1 . . . K—N1; 2 B—B5 and
wins.
2 B—B5ch   K—N4
3 P—KR4 mate

970   1 RxRPch!   PxR
2 N—N5ch   K—N1
3 Q—R6   P—B3
4 NxB   Q—R2
5 QxQch   KxQ
6 NxRch   RxN
7 RxBP   Resigns
White has two extra Pawns with
an easy win.

971   1 Q—R6!   PxQ
2 R—N8 mate

972   1 RxPch!   KxR
2 N—R5ch   K—B1
If 2 . . . K—N3; 3 Q—K3! forces
a quick mate.
If 2 . . . K—R1; 3 NxN, Q—K4;
4 B—N2! is decisive.
3 NxN   NxN
4 QxN   K—K1
5 B—N5ch   Resigns
If 5 . . . K—Q1; 6 Q—R8ch,
K—B2; 7 B—KB4ch wins; or 5
. . . R—Q2; 6 Q—R8ch, K—K2;
7 B—N5ch, K—Q3; 8 B—KB4ch.

973   1 Q—R8ch!   KxR
2 R—K1ch   K—Q3
3 Q—K5 mate

974 1 Q—KR4!   R—K1
If 1 . . . PxB; 2 NxP with a
mating attack.
    2 BxRP!   PxB
    3 QxP   N—N3
    4 N—N5   N—B1
    5 R—K1!   P—Q4
If 5 . . . N—K3; 6 N—K4! wins.
    6 BxR   QxB
    7 R—K3   B—K3
    8 N—R7!   Resigns
There is no defense to the com-
ing R—N3ch.

975 1 QxN!   PxQ
    2 RxRch   KxR
    3 N—B6ch   K—B2
    4 NxQ   Resigns
White remains a piece ahead, for
if 4 . . . BxN; 5 RxN.

976 1 RxP!   KxR
    2 QxPch   K—K1
    3 B—N5!   Resigns
White threatens 4 QxB mate, and
3 . . . BxB is impossible because of
4 BxP mate.
If 3 . . . Q—B2; 4 BxPch, K—
Q2; 5 QxBch, K—B1; 6 B—B5ch
winning the Rook.

977 1 NxP!   BxP
If 1 . . . PxN; 2 RxPch wins
the Queen.
    2 Q—B3ch!   R/B1—B3
If 2 . . . B—K4; 3 N—B3 dis
ch and wins.
    3 N—K4 dis ch!   BxR
    4 RxBch   K—R1
If 4 . . . K—B1; 5 Q—N4ch
wins.
    5 QxRch!   RxQ
    6 R—N8ch!   KxR
    7 NxRch   K—B1
    8 NxQ   Resigns

978 1 RxPch!   PxR
    2 QxBPch   K—N1
    3 QxN   Q—B1
    4 N—K5!   Resigns
White has too many threats.

979 1 ....   N—B6ch!
    2 PxN   Q—R5
    3 R—R1   BxP!
    4 B—Q2   R—B3
         Resigns
White is helpless against 5 . . .
R—N3. If 5 KR—N1, B—B8 mate.

980 1 ....   BxP!
If now 2 PxB, Q—K6ch wins the
Queen.
    2 BxN   BxBPch
    3 KxB   QxPch
    4 K—B1   BxB
         Resigns

981 1 ....   B—K6ch!
If now 2 K—R1, R—R7 mate or
. . . B—N7 mate.
    2 RxB   R—Q8ch
    3 R—K1   RxR mate

982 1 ....   RxRP!
    2 N—B1   R—R8ch!
    3 KxR   R—R4ch
    4 K—N1   Q—R5
    5 N—N3   Q—R7ch
    6 K—B1   Q—R8ch!
    7 NxQ   RxN mate

983 1 ....   N—K7ch!
    2 RxN   R—B8ch!
    3 KxR   Q—R8ch
    4 K—B2   N—N5 mate

984 1 ....   N—B6ch!
If now 2 K—R1, R—R4; 3 P—
R3, BxP and wins.
    2 PxN   R—N4ch
    3 K—R1   QxP mate

985 1 ....   N—B6ch!
    2 PxN   ....
On 2 K B1, the most effective
is 2 . . . NxPch!
    2 ....   R—N4ch
If now 3 K—R1, QxBP leads to
mate.
    3 K—B1   Q—R6ch
    4 K—K2   R—K4 mate

986 1 ....   QxPch!
    2 KxQ   R—R3ch
    3 K—N3   N—K7ch!
    4 K—N4   R—B5ch
    5 K—N5   R—R7!
Threatens . . . P—R3 mate.
    6 QxNch   KxQ
    7 N—KB3   P—R3ch
    8 K—N6   K—N1!
Threatens . . . R—B3 mate.
    9 NxR   R—B4!
If now 10 P—KN3, R—N4 mate.
    10 PxR   N—B5 mate

987 1 ....   BxPch!
    2 KxB   QxRPch
    3 K—N1   P—N6!

4 P—B3   P—N7
5 K—B2   P—N8/Qch
6 RxQ   Q—R7ch
   Resigns
Black wins the Rook.

988 1 ....   BxP!
   If now 2 NxP, RxPch!; 3 KxR,
Q—Q7ch; 4 K—R3, Q—R3ch followed by mate.
    2 Q—B3   P—N4!
   If now 3 R—B8, P—N5 mate.
    3 P—KN4   PxN!
   If now 4 R—B8, B—N7 mate.
    4 P—N5   B—N2!
    5 K—N4   Q—Q4
     Resigns

989 1 ....   R—N8ch!
    2 RxR   Q—QB6ch
And mate next move.

990 1 ....   BxPch!
    2 QxB   R—N6!
    3 QxB   ....
   If 3 QxQ, RxRP mate.
    3 ....   R—N7 dbl ch
And mate next move.

991 1 ....   Q—B6ch
    2 B—N3   P—N4!
   Threatens . . . Q—B8 mate. If
now 3 R—Q2, Q—B8ch; 4 R—N2,
P—R4; 5 PxP, QxP mate.
    3 PxP e. p.   K—N4!
   Again threatening . . . Q—B8
mate.
    4 R—Q2   P—R4!
    5 PxP   Q—B8ch
    6 R—N2   Q—B4 mate

992 1 ....   R—KR4!
   If now 2 P—N3, QxP; 3 B—K4,
RxR; 4 RxR, NxB; 5 PxN, BxPch
etc.
    2 P—KR3   N—N5!
    3 BPxN   RxPch
    4 K—N1   Q—R7ch
    5 K—B1   Q—R8ch
Followed by 6 QxP mate.

993 1 ....   QxRPch
    2 K—N1   Q—R8ch
    3 K—B2   Q—R7ch
Black wins the Queen.

994 1 ....   RxPch!
    2 KxR   Q—R6ch
    3 K—B2   Q—R7ch
    4 K—B3   R—KB1ch
    5 Q—B7   RxQ mate

995 1 ....   RxPch!
    2 KxR   Q—R6ch
    3 K—N1   R—N1ch
    4 N—N3   RxNch!
    5 PxR   B—KB4ch
And Black wins the Queen.

996 1 ....   N—B6ch!
    2 PxN   B/N5xP dis ch
    3 B—N3   QxBch!
    4 PxQ   RxPch
    5 K—R2   ....
   Or 5 B—N2, RxBch followed by
. . . R—R7 and . . . R—R8 mate.
    5 ....   BxP
    6 B—R3   RxBch!
    7 KxR   R—R1 mate

997 1 ....   N—B6ch!
   If now 2 PxN, Q—N4ch or . . .
R—N4ch leads to mate.
    2 K—R1   Q—R5
    3 P—R3   N—K8!
     Resigns
   Black attacks the Queen and also
threatens 4 . . . QxRPch followed
by . . . QxP mate.

998 1 ....   NxRP!
   If now 2 PxN, QxPch; 3 K—N1,
R—N6ch and mate in two more
moves.
    2 PxR   N—B7 dis ch
    3 K—N3   Q—R6ch!
   If now 4 KxN, Q—R7ch wins
the Queen.
    4 K—B4   Q—R7ch
    5 K—K3   N—N5ch!
     Resigns
   If 6 K—Q3, N—K4ch wins the
Queen. And if 6 PxN, QxQ wins.

999 1 ....   Q—N8ch!
    2 RxQ   N—B7 mate

1000 1 ....   N—B5!
   Threatens 2 . . . N—R6 mate. If
2 PxN, BxBP, 3 R—K3, BxPch!
forcing mate.
    2 P—KR4   QxP!
     Resigns
   If 3 PxQ, N—R6 mate.

1001 1 ....   Q—B8ch!
    2 B—N1   Q—B6ch!
    3 BxQ   BxB mate
   This very beautiful combination,
played in a blindfold exhibition of
22 games by the great Pillsbury,
worthily concludes our collection.

A PERSONAL WORD FROM MELVIN POWERS
PUBLISHER, WILSHIRE BOOK COMPANY

Dear Friend:

My goal is to publish interesting, informative, and inspirational books. You can help me accomplish this by answering the following questions, either by phone or by mail. Or, if convenient for you, I would welcome the opportunity to visit with you in my office and hear your comments in person.

Did you enjoy reading this book? Why?

Would you enjoy reading another similar book?

What idea in the book impressed you the most?

If applicable to your situation, have you incorporated this idea in your daily life?

Is there a chapter that could serve as a theme for an entire book? Please explain.

If you have an idea for a book, I would welcome discussing it with you. If you already have one in progress, write or call me concerning possible publication. I can be reached at (213) 875-1711 or (213) 983-1105.

Sincerely yours,

MELVIN POWERS

12015 Sherman Road
North Hollywood, California 91605

MELVIN POWERS SELF-IMPROVEMENT LIBRARY

ASTROLOGY

____ ASTROLOGY: HOW TO CHART YOUR HOROSCOPE *Max Heindel*
____ ASTROLOGY: YOUR PERSONAL SUN-SIGN GUIDE *Beatrice Ryder*
____ ASTROLOGY FOR EVERYDAY LIVING *Janet Harris*
____ ASTROLOGY MADE EASY *Astarte*
____ ASTROLOGY MADE PRACTICAL *Alexandra Kayhle*
____ ASTROLOGY, ROMANCE, YOU AND THE STARS *Anthony Norvell*
____ MY WORLD OF ASTROLOGY *Sydney Omarr*
____ THOUGHT DIAL *Sidney Omarr*
____ WHAT THE STARS REVEAL ABOUT THE MEN IN YOUR LIFE *Thelma White*

BRIDGE

____ BRIDGE BIDDING MADE EASY *Edwin B. Kantar*
____ BRIDGE CONVENTIONS *Edwin B. Kantar*
____ BRIDGE HUMOR *Edwin B. Kantar*
____ COMPETITIVE BIDDING IN MODERN BRIDGE *Edgar Kaplan*
____ DEFENSIVE BRIDGE PLAY COMPLETE *Edwin B. Kantar*
____ GAMESMAN BRIDGE—Play Better with Kantar *Edwin B. Kantar*
____ HOW TO IMPROVE YOUR BRIDGE *Alfred Sheinwold*
____ IMPROVING YOUR BIDDING SKILLS *Edwin B. Kantar*
____ INTRODUCTION TO DECLARER'S PLAY *Edwin B. Kantar*
____ INTRODUCTION TO DEFENDER'S PLAY *Edwin B. Kantar*
____ KANTAR FOR THE DEFENSE *Edwin B. Kantar*
____ SHORT CUT TO WINNING BRIDGE *Alfred Sheinwold*
____ TEST YOUR BRIDGE PLAY *Edwin B. Kantar*
____ VOLUME 2—TEST YOUR BRIDGE PLAY *Edwin B. Kantar*
____ WINNING DECLARER PLAY *Dorothy Hayden Truscott*

BUSINESS, STUDY & REFERENCE

____ CONVERSATION MADE EASY *Elliot Russell*
____ EXAM SECRET *Dennis B. Jackson*
____ FIX-IT BOOK *Arthur Symons*
____ HOW TO DEVELOP A BETTER SPEAKING VOICE *M. Hellier*
____ HOW TO MAKE A FORTUNE IN REAL ESTATE *Albert Winnikoff*
____ INCREASE YOUR LEARNING POWER *Geoffrey A. Dudley*
____ MAGIC OF NUMBERS *Robert Tocquet*
____ PRACTICAL GUIDE TO BETTER CONCENTRATION *Melvin Powers*
____ PRACTICAL GUIDE TO PUBLIC SPEAKING *Maurice Forley*
____ 7 DAYS TO FASTER READING *William S. Schaill*
____ SONGWRITERS' RHYMING DICTIONARY *Jane Shaw Whitfield*
____ SPELLING MADE EASY *Lester D. Basch & Dr. Milton Finkelstein*
____ STUDENT'S GUIDE TO BETTER GRADES *J. A. Rickard*
____ TEST YOURSELF—Find Your Hidden Talent *Jack Shafer*
____ YOUR WILL & WHAT TO DO ABOUT IT *Attorney Samuel G. Kling*

CALLIGRAPHY

____ ADVANCED CALLIGRAPHY *Katherine Jeffares*
____ CALLIGRAPHER'S REFERENCE BOOK *Anne Leptich & Jacque Evans*
____ CALLIGRAPHY—The Art of Beautiful Writing *Katherine Jeffares*
____ CALLIGRAPHY FOR FUN & PROFIT *Anne Leptich & Jacque Evans*
____ CALLIGRAPHY MADE EASY *Tina Serafini*

CHESS & CHECKERS

____ BEGINNER'S GUIDE TO WINNING CHESS *Fred Reinfeld*
____ CHECKERS MADE EASY *Tom Wiswell*
____ CHESS IN TEN EASY LESSONS *Larry Evans*
____ CHESS MADE EASY *Milton L. Hanauer*
____ CHESS PROBLEMS FOR BEGINNERS *edited by Fred Reinfeld*
____ CHESS SECRETS REVEALED *Fred Reinfeld*
____ CHESS STRATEGY—An Expert's Guide *Fred Reinfeld*
____ CHESS TACTICS FOR BEGINNERS *edited by Fred Reinfeld*
____ CHESS THEORY & PRACTICE *Morry & Mitchell*
____ HOW TO WIN AT CHECKERS *Fred Reinfeld*
____ 1001 BRILLIANT WAYS TO CHECKMATE *Fred Reinfeld*

_ 1001 WINNING CHESS SACRIFICES & COMBINATIONS *Fred Reinfeld*	4.00
_ SOVIET CHESS *Edited by R. G. Wade*	3.00

COOKERY & HERBS

_ CULPEPER'S HERBAL REMEDIES *Dr. Nicholas Culpeper*	3.00
_ FAST GOURMET COOKBOOK *Poppy Cannon*	2.50
_ GINSENG The Myth & The Truth *Joseph P. Hou*	3.00
_ HEALING POWER OF HERBS *May Bethel*	4.00
_ HEALING POWER OF NATURAL FOODS *May Bethel*	4.00
_ HERB HANDBOOK *Dawn MacLeod*	3.00
_ HERBS FOR COOKING AND HEALING *Dr. Donald Law*	2.00
_ HERBS FOR HEALTH—How to Grow & Use Them *Louise Evans Doole*	3.00
_ HOME GARDEN COOKBOOK—Delicious Natural Food Recipes *Ken Kraft*	3.00
_ MEDICAL HERBALIST *edited by Dr. J. R. Yemm*	3.00
_ NATURAL FOOD COOKBOOK *Dr. Harry C. Bond*	3.00
_ NATURE'S MEDICINES *Richard Lucas*	3.00
_ VEGETABLE GARDENING FOR BEGINNERS *Hugh Wiberg*	2.00
_ VEGETABLES FOR TODAY'S GARDENS *R. Milton Carleton*	2.00
_ VEGETARIAN COOKERY *Janet Walker*	4.00
_ VEGETARIAN COOKING MADE EASY & DELECTABLE *Veronica Vezza*	3.00
_ VEGETARIAN DELIGHTS—A Happy Cookbook for Health *K. R. Mehta*	2.00
_ VEGETARIAN GOURMET COOKBOOK *Joyce McKinnel*	3.00

GAMBLING & POKER

_ ADVANCED POKER STRATEGY & WINNING PLAY *A. D. Livingston*	5.00
_ HOW NOT TO LOSE AT POKER *Jeffrey Lloyd Castle*	3.00
_ HOW TO WIN AT DICE GAMES *Skip Frey*	3.00
_ HOW TO WIN AT POKER *Terence Reese & Anthony T. Watkins*	3.00
_ SECRETS OF WINNING POKER *George S. Coffin*	3.00
_ WINNING AT CRAPS *Dr. Lloyd T. Commins*	3.00
_ WINNING AT GIN *Chester Wander & Cy Rice*	3.00
_ WINNING AT POKER—An Expert's Guide *John Archer*	3.00
_ WINNING AT 21—An Expert's Guide *John Archer*	5.00
_ WINNING POKER SYSTEMS *Norman Zadeh*	3.00

HEALTH

_ BEE POLLEN *Lynda Lyngheim & Jack Scagnetti*	3.00
_ DR. LINDNER'S SPECIAL WEIGHT CONTROL METHOD *P. G. Lindner, M.D.*	2.00
_ HELP YOURSELF TO BETTER SIGHT *Margaret Darst Corbett*	3.00
_ HOW TO IMPROVE YOUR VISION *Dr. Robert A. Kraskin*	3.00
_ HOW YOU CAN STOP SMOKING PERMANENTLY *Ernest Caldwell*	3.00
_ MIND OVER PLATTER *Peter G. Lindner, M.D.*	3.00
_ NATURE'S WAY TO NUTRITION & VIBRANT HEALTH *Robert J. Scrutton*	3.00
_ NEW CARBOHYDRATE DIET COUNTER *Patti Lopez-Pereira*	1.50
_ QUICK & EASY EXERCISES FOR FACIAL BEAUTY *Judy Smith-deal*	2.00
_ QUICK & EASY EXERCISES FOR FIGURE BEAUTY *Judy Smith-deal*	2.00
_ REFLEXOLOGY *Dr. Maybelle Segal*	3.00
_ REFLEXOLOGY FOR GOOD HEALTH *Anna Kaye & Don C. Matchan*	3.00
_ YOU CAN LEARN TO RELAX *Dr. Samuel Gutwirth*	3.00
_ YOUR ALLERGY—What To Do About It *Allan Knight, M.D.*	3.00

HOBBIES

_ BEACHCOMBING FOR BEGINNERS *Norman Hickin*	2.00
_ BLACKSTONE'S MODERN CARD TRICKS *Harry Blackstone*	3.00
_ BLACKSTONE'S SECRETS OF MAGIC *Harry Blackstone*	3.00
_ COIN COLLECTING FOR BEGINNERS *Burton Hobson & Fred Reinfeld*	3.00
_ ENTERTAINING WITH ESP *Tony 'Doc' Shiels*	2.00
_ 400 FASCINATING MAGIC TRICKS YOU CAN DO *Howard Thurston*	4.00
_ HOW I TURN JUNK INTO FUN AND PROFIT *Sari*	3.00
_ HOW TO WRITE A HIT SONG & SELL IT *Tommy Boyce*	7.00
_ JUGGLING MADE EASY *Rudolf Dittrich*	2.00
_ MAGIC FOR ALL AGES *Walter Gibson*	4.00
_ MAGIC MADE EASY *Byron Wels*	2.00
_ STAMP COLLECTING FOR BEGINNERS *Burton Hobson*	3.00

HORSE PLAYERS' WINNING GUIDES

_ BETTING HORSES TO WIN *Les Conklin*	3.00
_ ELIMINATE THE LOSERS *Bob McKnight*	3.00

_ HOW TO RAISE AN EMOTIONALLY HEALTHY, HAPPY CHILD A. Ellis	4.00
_ SEX WITHOUT GUILT Albert Ellis, Ph.D.	5.00
_ SEXUALLY ADEQUATE MALE Frank S. Caprio, M.D.	3.00
_ SEXUALLY FULFILLED MAN Dr. Rachel Copelan	5.00

MELVIN POWERS' MAIL ORDER LIBRARY

_ HOW TO GET RICH IN MAIL ORDER Melvin Powers	10.00
_ HOW TO WRITE A GOOD ADVERTISEMENT Victor O. Schwab	15.00
_ MAIL ORDER MADE EASY J. Frank Brumbaugh	10.00
_ U.S. MAIL ORDER SHOPPER'S GUIDE Susan Spitzer	10.00

METAPHYSICS & OCCULT

_ BOOK OF TALISMANS, AMULETS & ZODIACAL GEMS William Pavitt	5.00
_ CONCENTRATION—A Guide to Mental Mastery Mouni Sadhu	4.00
_ CRITIQUES OF GOD Edited by Peter Angeles	7.00
_ EXTRA-TERRESTRIAL INTELLIGENCE—The First Encounter	6.00
_ FORTUNE TELLING WITH CARDS P. Foli	3.00
_ HANDWRITING ANALYSIS MADE EASY John Marley	4.00
_ HANDWRITING TELLS Nadya Olyanova	5.00
_ HOW TO INTERPRET DREAMS, OMENS & FORTUNE TELLING SIGNS Gettings	3.00
_ HOW TO UNDERSTAND YOUR DREAMS Geoffrey A. Dudley	3.00
_ ILLUSTRATED YOGA William Zorn	3.00
_ IN DAYS OF GREAT PEACE Mouni Sadhu	3.00
_ LSD—THE AGE OF MIND Bernard Roseman	2.00
_ MAGICIAN—His Training and Work W. E. Butler	3.00
_ MEDITATION Mouni Sadhu	5.00
_ MODERN NUMEROLOGY Morris C. Goodman	3.00
_ NUMEROLOGY—ITS FACTS AND SECRETS Ariel Yvon Taylor	3.00
_ NUMEROLOGY MADE EASY W. Mykian	3.00
_ PALMISTRY MADE EASY Fred Gettings	3.00
_ PALMISTRY MADE PRACTICAL Elizabeth Daniels Squire	4.00
_ PALMISTRY SECRETS REVEALED Henry Frith	3.00
_ PROPHECY IN OUR TIME Martin Ebon	2.50
_ PSYCHOLOGY OF HANDWRITING Nadya Olyanova	5.00
_ SUPERSTITION—Are You Superstitious? Eric Maple	2.00
_ TAROT Mouni Sadhu	6.00
_ TAROT OF THE BOHEMIANS Papus	5.00
_ WAYS TO SELF-REALIZATION Mouni Sadhu	3.00
_ WHAT YOUR HANDWRITING REVEALS Albert E. Hughes	3.00
_ WITCHCRAFT, MAGIC & OCCULTISM—A Fascinating History W. B. Crow	5.00
_ WITCHCRAFT—THE SIXTH SENSE Justine Glass	5.00
_ WORLD OF PSYCHIC RESEARCH Hereward Carrington	2.00

SELF-HELP & INSPIRATIONAL

_ DAILY POWER FOR JOYFUL LIVING Dr. Donald Curtis	5.00
_ DYNAMIC THINKING Melvin Powers	2.00
_ EXUBERANCE—Your Guide to Happiness & Fulfillment Dr. Paul Kurtz	3.00
_ GREATEST POWER IN THE UNIVERSE U. S. Andersen	5.00
_ GROW RICH WHILE YOU SLEEP Ben Sweetland	3.00
_ GROWTH THROUGH REASON Albert Ellis, Ph.D.	4.00
_ GUIDE TO DEVELOPING YOUR POTENTIAL Herbert A. Otto, Ph.D.	3.00
_ GUIDE TO LIVING IN BALANCE Frank S. Caprio, M.D.	2.00
_ GUIDE TO PERSONAL HAPPINESS Albert Ellis, Ph.D. & Irving Becker, Ed. D.	5.00
_ HELPING YOURSELF WITH APPLIED PSYCHOLOGY R. Henderson	2.00
_ HELPING YOURSELF WITH PSYCHIATRY Frank S. Caprio, M.D.	2.00
_ HOW TO ATTRACT GOOD LUCK A. H. Z. Carr	4.00
_ HOW TO CONTROL YOUR DESTINY Norvell	3.00
_ HOW TO DEVELOP A WINNING PERSONALITY Martin Panzer	5.00
_ HOW TO DEVELOP AN EXCEPTIONAL MEMORY Young & Gibson	4.00
_ HOW TO LIVE WITH A NEUROTIC Albert Ellis, Ph. D.	5.00
_ HOW TO OVERCOME YOUR FEARS M. P. Leahy, M.D.	3.00
_ HOW YOU CAN HAVE CONFIDENCE AND POWER Les Giblin	3.00
_ HUMAN PROBLEMS & HOW TO SOLVE THEM Dr. Donald Curtis	4.00
_ I CAN Ben Sweetland	5.00
_ I WILL Ben Sweetland	3.00
_ LEFT-HANDED PEOPLE Michael Barsley	4.00

The books listed above can be obtained from your book dealer or directly from Melvin Powers. When ordering, please remit 50¢ per book postage & handling. Send for our free illustrated catalog of self-improvement books.

Melvin Powers

12015 Sherman Road, No. Hollywood, California 91605

WILSHIRE HORSE LOVERS' LIBRARY

_____ AMATEUR HORSE BREEDER *A. C. Leighton Hardman*	4.00
_____ AMERICAN QUARTER HORSE IN PICTURES *Margaret Cabell Self*	3.00
_____ APPALOOSA HORSE *Donna & Bill Richardson*	5.00
_____ ARABIAN HORSE *Reginald S. Summerhays*	3.00
_____ ART OF WESTERN RIDING *Suzanne Norton Jones*	3.00
_____ AT THE HORSE SHOW *Margaret Cabell Self*	3.00
_____ BACK-YARD HORSE *Peggy Jett Pittinger*	4.00
_____ BASIC DRESSAGE *Jean Froissard*	2.00
_____ BEGINNER'S GUIDE TO HORSEBACK RIDING *Sheila Wall*	2.00
_____ BEGINNER'S GUIDE TO THE WESTERN HORSE *Natlee Kenoyer*	2.00
_____ BITS—THEIR HISTORY, USE AND MISUSE *Louis Taylor*	5.00
_____ BREAKING & TRAINING THE DRIVING HORSE *Doris Ganton*	3.00
_____ BREAKING YOUR HORSE'S BAD HABITS *W. Dayton Sumner*	5.00
_____ COMPLETE TRAINING OF HORSE AND RIDER *Colonel Alois Podhajsky*	5.00
_____ DISORDERS OF THE HORSE & WHAT TO DO ABOUT THEM *E. Hanauer*	3.00
_____ DOG TRAINING MADE EASY & FUN *John W. Kellogg*	4.00
_____ DRESSAGE—A Study of the Finer Points in Riding *Henry Wynmalen*	5.00
_____ DRIVE ON *Doris Ganton*	7.00
_____ DRIVING HORSES *Sallie Walrond*	3.00
_____ ENDURANCE RIDING *Ann Hyland*	2.00
_____ EQUITATION *Jean Froissard*	5.00
_____ FIRST AID FOR HORSES *Dr. Charles H. Denning, Jr.*	3.00
_____ FUN OF RAISING A COLT *Rubye & Frank Griffith*	3.00
_____ FUN ON HORSEBACK *Margaret Caball Self*	4.00
_____ GYMKHANA GAMES *Natlee Kenoyer*	2.00
_____ HORSE DISEASES—Causes, Symptoms & Treatment *Dr. H. G. Belschner*	5.00
_____ HORSE OWNER'S CONCISE GUIDE *Elsie V. Hanauer*	2.00
_____ HORSE SELECTION & CARE FOR BEGINNERS *George H. Conn*	5.00
_____ HORSEBACK RIDING FOR BEGINNERS *Louis Taylor*	4.00
_____ HORSEBACK RIDING MADE EASY & FUN *Sue Henderson Coen*	5.00
_____ HORSES—Their Selection, Care & Handling *Margaret Cabell Self*	4.00
_____ HOW TO BUY A BETTER HORSE & SELL THE HORSE YOU OWN	3.00
_____ HOW TO ENJOY YOUR QUARTER HORSE *Willard H. Porter*	3.00
_____ HUNTER IN PICTURES *Margaret Cabell Self*	2.00
_____ ILLUSTRATED BOOK OF THE HORSE *S. Sidney* (8½″ × 11″)	10.00
_____ ILLUSTRATED HORSE MANAGEMENT—400 Illustrations *Dr. E. Mayhew*	6.00
_____ ILLUSTRATED HORSE TRAINING *Captain M. H. Hayes*	5.00
_____ ILLUSTRATED HORSEBACK RIDING FOR BEGINNERS *Jeanne Mellin*	3.00
_____ JUMPING—Learning & Teaching *Jean Froissard*	4.00
_____ KNOW ALL ABOUT HORSES *Harry Disston*	3.00
_____ LAME HORSE Cause, Symptoms & Treatment *Dr. James R. Rooney*	4.00
_____ LAW & YOUR HORSE *Edward H. Greene*	5.00
_____ LIPIZZANERS & THE SPANISH RIDING SCHOOL *W. Reuter* (4¼″ × 6″)	5.00
_____ MANUAL OF HORSEMANSHIP *Harold Black*	5.00
_____ MOVIE HORSES—The Fascinating Techniques of Training *Anthony Amaral*	2.00
_____ POLICE HORSES *Judith Campbell*	2.00
_____ PRACTICAL GUIDE TO HORSESHOEING	5.00
_____ PRACTICAL GUIDE TO OWNING YOUR OWN HORSE *Steven D. Price*	3.00
_____ PRACTICAL HORSE PSYCHOLOGY *Moyra Williams*	4.00
_____ PROBLEM HORSES Guide for Curing Serious Behavior Habits *Summerhays*	3.00
_____ REINSMAN OF THE WEST—BRIDLES & BITS *Ed Connell*	5.00
_____ RESCHOOLING THE THOROUGHBRED *Peggy Jett Pittinger*	3.00
_____ RIDE WESTERN *Louis Taylor*	4.00
_____ SCHOOLING YOUR YOUNG HORSE *George Wheatley*	3.00
_____ STABLE MANAGEMENT FOR THE OWNER-GROOM *George Wheatley*	4.00
_____ STALLION MANAGEMENT—A Guide for Stud Owners *A. C. Hardman*	3.00
_____ TEACHING YOUR HORSE TO JUMP *W. J. Froud*	2.00
_____ TRAINING YOUR HORSE TO SHOW *Neale Haley*	4.00
_____ TREATING COMMON DISEASES OF YOUR HORSE *Dr. George H. Conn*	5.00
_____ TREATING HORSE AILMENTS *G. W. Serth*	2.00
_____ YOU AND YOUR PONY *Pepper Mainwaring Healey* (8½″ × 11″)	6.00
_____ YOUR FIRST HORSE *George C. Saunders, M.D.*	3.00
_____ YOUR PONY BOOK *Hermann Wiederhold*	2.00

*The books listed above can be obtained from your book dealer or directly from
Melvin Powers. When ordering, please remit 50¢ per book postage & handling.
Send for our free illustrated catalog of self-improvement books.*

Melvin Powers
12015 Sherman Road, No. Hollywood, California 91605

Notes